MW00791183

The Space Race

A Captivating Guide to the Cold War Competition Between the United States and Soviet Union to Reach the Moon

Free Bonus from Captivating History (Available for a Limited time)

Hi History Lovers!

Now you have a chance to join our exclusive history list so you can get your first history ebook for free as well as discounts and a potential to get more history books for free! Simply visit the link below to join.

Captivatinghistory.com/ebook

Also, make sure to follow us on Facebook, Twitter and Youtube by searching for Captivating History.

Contents

Introduction

The Cold War is usually thought of in terms of fear, potential nuclear war, and espionage. While these were elements of the years between the end of World War II and the 1990s, the competition between the US and the USSR had some real benefits. Perhaps the best and most impressive accomplishments during this time resulted from the Space Race.

The Space Race was not something either side set out to win. Initially, the US and USSR were only interested in becoming militarily superior to each other. This competition started by accepting and overlooking the atrocities that the German scientists had enacted on their fellow men during World War II. The best German scientists were given another chance by both nations and many other countries. There is even a joke about this time that depicts the two sides bragging that their German scientists were better than the other's. The next few years revealed just why these scientists were often absorbed into other nations instead of standing trial with other Nazis.

Following the end of World War II, many nations fought to bring the German scientists—especially the German engineers—home to their countries. The scientists had been a major factor in the Germans' long-term success, and, ultimately, the US and the USSR ensured that the scientists were more evenly divided between the two superpowers. The USSR did not benefit from absorbing German scientists as much as the US because they already had a very adept and knowledgeable primary scientist who had been researching the possibilities of space most of his adult life—Sergei Korolev. The US made more use of their German scientists and the input of others from around the world. While one country worked in secret, the other was far more open. The US's desire to be transparent to help other nations understand what it was doing was the catalyst for the start of the Space Race. Since the USSR could see what the US was doing, it decided to show its superiority through successful firsts in space.

Within two decades of the end of World War II, the two superpowers engaged in a completely different competition. The second half of the 1950s and all the 1960s became a period in which humanity finally did what it had been dreaming of doing for millennia: going into space. When the USSR successfully launched *Sputnik* in 1957, the US realized it was not nearly as far ahead in the Space Race as anticipated. For much of the next decade, the USSR was consistently first in the race to get into space. It successfully sent the first person into space, then the first woman into space, and was the first to orbit the globe. It was even the first to land an artificial device on the moon in 1959. With the pressure on, the US began to focus more on space travel. The USSR had been first to reach the moon (as well as send the first life, including two tortoises, to the moon and back), but the US National Aeronautics and Space Administration (NASA) became the first agency to successfully send humans into the moon's orbit in 1968.

Then, in 1969, the US managed to do what was thought impossible just two decades earlier: it landed a man on the moon and successfully returned him to Earth. Forty years later, no other nations have managed to land a person on the moon.

Following this major success, the Space Race began to die down, and the two superpowers started focusing their attention and efforts elsewhere. Other problems were creating issues that were impossible to ignore back on Earth, and with the major first goals accomplished, it seemed like there wasn't much else to do. The Space Race had all but ended at this point, and it took decades before there was any further significant progress made in space travel. Many at the end of the 1960s could see humans reaching and colonizing Mars within the next fifty years. However, this was not to be the case. It was several decades before anyone even attempted to send orbiters to Mars.

With the crumbling of the USSR and the division of the superpower into several individual nations during the 1990s, the USSR was no longer able to participate in the Space Race. Instead of continuing to push each other through competition, the US and Russia began to work together. Attempts to explore space slowed down but never fully stopped. During the early part of the 21ˢ century, many other nations began to look toward space to see what they could do. By 2020, there was a new Space Race, with several nations trying to achieve what the US and USSR had achieved several decades earlier. This new Space Race has helped revive an interest in space travel on a different level: some private companies have begun to realize their agency to accomplish something that previously was only possible through an entire nation's efforts.

Chapter 1 – The End of World War II, the Fate of German Scientists, and the Future of an Unassuming Ukrainian

Even before World War II began, German scientists had a reputation for their innovation and ability to solve problems. They provided the Germans with a real military advantage through the weapons they devised, including nerve and disease agents. They used psychological warfare to lower the morale of the Allies. When the Allies finally defeated the Nazis and trekked through Germany and the regions the Nazis had occupied, the Allied countries were shocked by the kinds of weapons the scientists had been creating. From a weaponized form of the bubonic plague to other inventions the Allies had not even considered developing, it quickly became apparent to the military leaders that they bringing the inventive German scientists back to their respective countries would give them a distinct advantage. This was particularly true for two emerging superpowers in the post-World War II world: the US and the USSR. The tense friendship that had been maintained during the war ended when it became clear the Nazis had been defeated. Neither side trusted the other, and without an enemy to unify them, the US and USSR began to square off, each promoting its own ideas about what was the best form of governance. In reality, the problem ran much deeper.

At this point, the world was tired of open war. World Wars I and II had left the world unwilling to engage in further combat, especially over something as abstract as ideology. Neither the US nor the USSR wanted to engage in open warfare. Following the end of World War II, both began to look for a different way to wage war that would not cost the lives of soldiers, one in which they could achieve domination through means other than military strength.

The result was a competition to see who could acquire the highest number of former Nazi scientists. In the US, Operation Paperclip was born. This intelligence program brought German scientists into the country, largely in secret. As word spread of the horrors committed by the Nazis in concentration camps, the US government realized the problems that could arise if they were open about bringing German scientists home. The USSR faced a similar problem, especially with the additional level of animosity between the Soviets and Germans. However, both governments decided that bringing such imaginative scientists into their own countries was worth the advantage it would give them in the kinds of weapons they could develop. In total, the US brought eighty-eight Nazi scientists back to the country. It is less certain how many scientists were brought into the USSR, as they were notoriously secretive.

Both countries tried to minimize the activities of their scientists during the time they served under the Nazis. In some instances, the scientists simply did what they were required to do under a ruthless regiment. There were some scientists in the group who had only done what was necessary to ensure they were not killed and their loved ones were left alone. However, it is also true that some of the scientists that both the US and USSR smuggled home were guilty of some real atrocities, whether in the name of self-preservation or indifference. Both nations decided it was more important to have a weapons advantage over each other than to hold these scientists accountable for the atrocities they oversaw.

One of the most notable scientists who was rescued—perhaps without deserving a second chance—was Wernher von Braun. What is interesting about von Braun's time in the US is that, without him, the events of the next few decades would have likely played out very differently. The Nazis had been focused on much more than just weaponry. Back in 1936, they had telecasted the Olympic Games, which were being hosted in Germany. Though not the first broadcast, it was the first to use high frequency signals that likely reached space. While not quite the same as what was to come, this showed that Germany had focused on improving technology overall, not just advancing their weaponry. The US and USSR soon made use of impressive technological advances the Germans had made over the course of the war.

The other notable scientist in the Space Race was Sergei Korolev, a Ukrainian who eventually became another victim of Stalin's paranoia. However, he left his mark on the direction of the space race in the USSR, giving the union a distinct advantage in the race that came to dominate the news around the world during most of the 1960s. Korolev was the man who provided the first real successes of the Space Race.

Wernher von Braun

When it became clear Germany was going to lose the war, its scientists (and many in the military) knew it was only a matter of time before they were captured by Allied troops. There had long been a terrible relationship between the Russians and the Germans, so many German scientists sought to surrender to American, British, or French soldiers. They feared the way they would likely be treated by the Russians more than the way the nations attacked by Germany would treat them. Wernher von Braun was one of these scientists, and he turned himself over to the Allies in 1945. The Soviets took over the

German rocket testing facility in Peenemünde, where von Braun had worked.

Von Braun was the son of a civil servant, born into a noble Prussian family that had supplied many military officers to its country. This meant he had more privileges than the average German or Austrian and likely had a very different understanding of how the government served the people. When he received a telescope for his 13th birthday, he became very interested in space and the possibility of space travel—to the point of neglecting school classes that didn't further his interests. Understandably, this upset his family. Still, he managed to advance more quickly through school because of how easily he learned math and science. He joined the Verein für Raumschiffahrt, a group for people with interest in rocket science. As a part of this society, he gained the attention of the rising German army in 1932. The army offered von Braun a military position to further develop his skills, and he joined. He also started his doctoral program at the University of Berlin. He was hardly aware of the Nazis when they came to power in 1933 because his focus was still almost exclusively on his project: twenty-one-year-old von Braun was often lost in a world of his own.

Von Braun was the technical director of the German project to produce V-2 ballistic missiles, which were constructed by people in concentration camps. Von Braun had been to the facility where the ballistic missile was being made several times as the director of Peenemünde. Both the US government and von Braun himself portrayed his role as a Nazi scientist as apolitical, stating he had done what was necessary to achieve his goal of making it to space. He was called to give an interview for the West German consulate in late 1968 about his time working for the Nazis, and he did give this interview in 1969 during a trial of several Schutzstaffel (SS) personnel. The actual records of his time as a Nazi were released during the 1980s, eight years after he died. It became clear that, far from the political victim he and the US government portrayed, von Braun had been very much aware of where the labor at the facility had come from (even though he had not been involved in the formation of the concentration camp that dedicated workers to the facility). He said that he had been aware of the deplorable conditions and had even negotiated to have some of the personnel transferred so he could help Charles Sadron, a French physicist who had been taken prisoner. While this implicated him in some of the Nazis' crimes against humanity, it was also clear he had been forced to walk a very thin line during his employment for the tyrannical regime. He was arrested by the Gestapo for ten days in 1944 and is often said to have made a Faustian bargain so he could work on a rocket. It seems he was not aware of just how much control the government would have over his project, realizing too late just what he had gotten himself into.

Following his surrender in 1945, von Braun was brought to the US and put to work at Fort Bliss near El Paso, Texas. His war record was covered up so he could continue his work in the US with other German scientists. The team was moved to Huntsville, Alabama, in 1950, where they built missiles. Eventually, von Braun became a big proponent of putting more effort toward space travel. His loyalty to Germany quickly disappeared, as the US made him an American citizen and gave him a prestigious position with control over a project building missiles and rockets.

Though his time with the Nazis has certainly tainted his legacy, there is no doubt that von Braun was instrumental in any success the US had in the Space Race. His interest in space did not diminish over time, and he was even concerned that his record would undermine NASA's reputation. It was partly due to this concern that he waited until after the successful Apollo 7 mission at the end of 1968 before he gave his interview regarding the SS military members.

Sergei Korolev

Unlike von Braun, Sergei Korolev was born to a Ukrainian teacher. Although his father taught Russian literature, Korolev found his interest in aviation. When he was seventeen years old, he designed a glider. When he entered the University of Moscow, this interest shifted to rocket science, which was then in its infancy. After founding the Group for the Study of Reactive Motion, Korolev developed what became the first Soviet rockets in 1931. By 1933, the Soviet military had taken control of the group, which then became the first official part of the development of missiles and other potential weapons. Korolev continued to focus on space while another scientist, Valentin Glushko, worked on propulsions.

After the group had achieved several successes, Stalin's Great Purge began, and Glushko was arrested. Hoping to get his sentence reduced, Glushko joined others in denouncing Korolev, who was then arrested in 1938. Though sentenced to ten years of hard labor, Korolev served less than three years (although he did spend four months in the Gulag). Another political prisoner, Andrei Tupolev, requested Korolev's assistance on projects the military allowed him to work on. Korolev was dedicated to the work, and by the end of 1944, he was put in charge of his own project: trying to make something comparable to the V2 missiles used by the Germans.

With the end of the war in 1945, the Soviets tried to capture German scientists. The US had managed to get many of the top members of the German teams, particularly Wernher von Braun. Still a political prisoner, Korolev was put in charge of a new research center with German scientists. He and his team developed the first intercontinental ballistic missile with a range of 7,000 km, far surpassing the German V2.

Sergei Korolev became known as the Father of the Soviet Union's success in space. However, he did not live to see his biggest success. After being diagnosed with cancer in 1965, he chose to undergo an operation. He died during that operation at the beginning of 1966. Within a month of his death, his project to land a craft on the moon succeeded. Without him, the Soviet space program suffered and began to fall behind the US's. Glushko, who had become Korolev's nemesis after getting him arrested, took over the projects but simply did not have the knowledge or abilities of the man he had once denounced. Even today, the Russians still use the plans Korolev had drawn up for future progress.

Chapter 2 – A Brief Overview of the Cold War Rivalry

Following World War II, there should have been a period of peace and restoration to normalcy. Instead, the world devolved into a tense period known as the Cold War. With most of the world seriously damaged by the war, there were two nations that rose to become rival superpowers: the US and the USSR.

The use of nuclear weapons by the US to end the war brought the world into an entirely new era. Once the USSR acquired that same technology, one of the most dangerous races in world history began: the Nuclear Arms Race. The tension and hostility saw the two nations take the world to the brink of disaster.

When people think of the Cold War, they think of nuclear weapons, the Space Race, spies, and a fight between capitalism and communism. While some of these visions are accurate, others are inaccurate. The fight between the two superpowers took a turn that, while not entirely new, pushed the idea of what was possible.

The End of One War, The Start of Another

Prior to World War II, the very diverse ideologies of the US and USSR inspired dislike between their people and governments, but as both countries pursued isolationist policies, they did not interact much. It was only after World War II that the two countries emerged, wanting to play a larger role on the world's stage.

World War II necessitated uneasy alliances, particularly following the violent overthrow of the Russian monarchy just a few decades earlier. Many of the Allies believed they had struck a bad deal with the rising Soviet Union because the Nazis were the immediate threat. Many of the European nations were devastated after World War II ended, so they were unable to participate in the Space Race. In reality, the USSR didn't have the funds to push for space either, and the Space Race would lead to its bankruptcy since it cost than they had anticipated. Western European nations focused on recovering and restoring thriving economies instead of joining in the push to get into space. The devastation would be their focus for roughly two decades following the end of the war. The fact that they had struck a deal with the USSR created considerable unease, especially as it seemed to recover so much faster from the war than the other nations.

Compared to the other nations who fought in World War II, the US had joined the war late, only entering at the end of 1941 when the Japanese forced its hand. The Soviet Union had also been slow to get involved in the war, having spent several months using the cover of the war to invade neighboring nations. After Stalin's 1935 attempt to form an alliance with other nations (many that later joined the Allies) was rejected, he formed an agreement with Hitler in 1939, making much of the rest of the western world even more anti-Soviet. Only when Hitler sent his military to invade the Soviet Union in 1941 did the two countries became openly hostile, and the Soviets finally joined the Allies.

With the dire situation across Europe and much of Europe under German control, the remaining free European countries did not have much choice. However, Stalin's former alliance with Hitler made it very difficult for the Allies to trust him, and this mistrust did not disappear just because Stalin was finally willing to work with them on their terms. Suspicion and wariness of Stalin continued even after the western nations began to work with the USSR.

The Soviets soon showed why fully trusting them was difficult. While fighting the Nazis, the Soviets continued to expand their area of control under the claim that they were "liberating" nations. Unable to face both the Soviets and the Germans, the Allies could do nothing to stop the hostile overthrow of smaller nations by the Soviets. The resemblances to the way Hitler had worked and what Stalin was doing was not missed by the rest of the Allies, and their mistrust only grew as the war continued. Europe had initially been willing to let Germany take several nations to keep the peace; they did not want to make that same mistake again.

Eastern Europe versus Western Europe

With the end of World War II, the mistrust between capitalist nations and the Soviets intensified. The war-torn nations of Europe were divided between East and West, including Germany, as the USSR insisted on gaining control over some of the countries. Unlike the other European nations, though, the USSR was more interested in growing its power base, not in helping those nations recover. No longer facing a common enemy to unite them with the USSR, Western Europe and the US turned against the aggressive advances of the Soviet Union. Stalin believed that the western European nations would quibble and he would be able to capitalize on this, expanding the USSR into the western parts of Europe. With so many of the western nations devastated from the war, the only other nation that could stand against the USSR was the US. The US provided support to help rebuild European nations, but it also worked to prevent the further spread of communism.

Tensions continued to grow, with Western Bloc nations working to contain communist influences, as stated by the US Congress in 1947. At the time, only the US had nuclear capabilities, and they hoped to use this to keep the Soviets in check. This containment strategy required aiding the western European nations, including Germany. After putting the Marshall Plan in place, the US sought to expand into other economic markets while also providing extensive economic aid. By helping the devastated nations regain control over their economies, the US hoped to ensure that the people in those nations didn't turn to communism to better their lives. It should be noted that what the Soviets called communism was a form of dictatorship, with Stalin clearly at the top. It was not communism as Lenin or Marx had taught it, and Lenin had even warned against letting Stalin get control before he died. Failing to make this distinction, the US worked to expand the system of capitalism when perhaps they should have adopted an approach similar to the strategy that had been used against Hitler. After all, the Soviet Union had grown through hostile invasions, not ideological conversions.

The Trajectory of the Cold War

Once the USSR became a nuclear power, with other nations quickly following suit, war as it had always been fought was no longer possible. Nuclear weapons were simply too deadly, and the launch of any nuclear weapons would likely result in overuse as more nations stockpiled these very destructive weapons. There was a very real possibility that any use of the weapons would trigger an end to humanity as other nations reacted by using their own weapons. Nations were also starting to realize just how much damage the nuclear weapons caused through fallout. Stockpiling these weapons and making them even more deadly was largely symbolic because most nations understood that using not them would result in dire consequences.

By 1950, the power blocs were in place, and both sides hated each other. While the US was the superpower for the West, European nations were joining in the fight against the USSR through other means. To the east, China was emulating Stalin's approach to communism as it finally ended its civil war and witnessed the rise of Mao Zedong. However, the US and the USSR were the nations with the most power, making them the two representatives of East and West. The idea isn't entirely accurate, as the US was helping to rebuild Japan, which was further east than either the USSR or China, as well as Australia, New Zealand, and other Asian nations with their own forms of government. This later came into play during the battle between the USSR and the US as they began to openly fight proxy wars.

Paranoia grew during this time, with either side believing that the other threatened its very way of life. With traditional war becoming far too dangerous, both sides resorted to other ways of striking at perceived threats. Spies have been around since war was invented, but they were relied upon to act as soldiers during the Cold War. It was easier to deny their existence or to simply trade them in private than to manage actual soldiers on the battlefield.

The Cold War spread well beyond Europe as the rest of the world began to recover following the end of World War II. China had been in political turmoil before the war started, but the factions had put their differences aside to fight the superior powers of the invading Japanese. Once the war was over, the two sides continued their civil war, resulting in the rise of Mao Zedong and Communist China. Like the USSR, China was a dictatorship or oligarchy, not a country that was communist by Marx or Lenin's definition. This was seen by the West as a sign that communism was spreading, fueling their fears.

However, the most interesting and obvious result of the Cold War was the drive to gain dominance in space. By smuggling home

German scientists who had been working on rocket technology since before World War II, both the US and the USSR gained significant advantages (though the USSR had a very good scientist of their own they were persecuting at this point). While the other aspects of the Cold War tended to be destructive, the Space Race pushed imagination to the forefront and gave people hope for the future.

Chapter 3 – A Grand Announcement: Both Nations Pledge to Launch Satellites

With both sides firmly established, the world's two superpowers began to try to showcase their abilities to the world to demonstrate which of the two ideologies was superior. Ultimately, their achievements weren't what persuaded nations to adopt one doctrine or the other, but they pushed science well ahead of what many people thought was possible at the time. The US had been the first country to create an atomic bomb, while the Soviet Union was still largely trying to find its footing after its upheaval. The Soviets had a very capable scientist in Sergei Korolev, but with the addition of the German scientists, the USSR quickly caught up to what the US had achieved during World War II. While weapons were important, both sides were focused on something that no nation had chased before the 1950s—the ability to go into space.

The Space Race created a way for the two nations to compete in a way that was far less terrifying and far more engaging than the horrific weaponry they were also developing. Both sides tended to be secretive about the types of weapons they were developing for warfare, but over time, the USSR began to publish more information about its accomplishments.

The positive news of the race to achieve a host of first in space accolades helped ease the tension the two nations had created around the world. Whereas people feared what could happen if there was a nuclear war, the race to be the first to accomplish various milestones in space stimulated the imagination. The Space Race was a positive aspect of the Cold War that is still felt today, as many nations work to go further into space and accomplish new firsts long after it had ended.

Though both nations were working on developing ways to reach space, the Space Race did not begin as a way of encouraging each other. Instead, it was a way of gaining military superiority. However, scientists were often much more interested in the travel aspect, leading the focus to be more on what was possible than how best to use space as a new arena to fight in (and maybe over).

Two Sides Prepare

The beginning of the Space Race wasn't exactly planned. As the two nations eyed each other suspiciously, they were developing missiles, ballistics, and aircraft that would give them an advantage if another war started. The weapons they created were largely deterrents to war because the leaders from both sides understood that the risks of using their most powerful weapons were too high.

The USSR had a head start toward developing ballistic missiles, thanks to Korolev's work. During 1954, he had been instructed to work on an intercontinental ballistic missile, which would have been a first of its kind for the USSR. The missile was named the R-7. While the government was interested in weaponry, Korolev was interested in pursuing his interest in space. After his initial research, Korolev had a coworker and friend named Mikhail Klavdiyevich Tikhonravov write the *Report on an Artificial Satellite of the Earth* to suggest that the ballistic missile could be used to launch satellites. If he could convince the government that the work could double as a means of establishing a position in space, it would give him a way to keep studying his own passion. To persuade the Russian government to adopt his idea, Korolev included some documents about the US interest in space and their work. Since the US was far more open about what they were doing, it gave Korolev a way to stoke some of the Russian paranoia and persuade the government that it should be considering more than just missiles: it needed to start thinking in terms of what space exploration could do for the USSR.

Though the US hadn't gotten as far as Korolev, it had been steadily working toward getting satellites into space since the early part of the 1950s because people in the US were very interested in space exploration. Ever since the panic inspired by Orson Welles' *War of the Worlds* broadcast over the radio in 1938, interest in aliens and what could be found in space had inspired Americans' imaginations. The US military had been studying the possibility of sending a satellite into space, though it was more of a question of how to do it rather than whether it was possible. The US had released the *Beacon Hill Report* in 1952, a study with fifteen different authors who had worked at the Massachusetts Institute of Technology to do reconnaissance. The report found that satellites that went over the USSR or their territories could be considered a breach of sovereignty. The US had considered conducting its own satellite launches, but this possible violation led to the determination that the satellite launches would need to be approved by a higher authority—namely, the US president.

Just a few years later, another report titled the *Meeting the Threat of Surprise Attack* was released by the Technological Capabilities Panel (a committee formed by the Office of Defense Mobilization). It concurred with the idea that a higher authority was needed to approve launches. To address this, the president's administration wanted to establish a "freedom of space" principle that would allow for the launch of military satellites. By this point, President Dwight D. Eisenhower was listening, and his administration quickly adopted the principle. It had already become a popular discussion topic within scientific circles, so most were prepared for the US government to finally embrace the idea. The same year that Korolev was working to persuade the USSR government to embrace the idea of the dual importance of satellites, the US-sponsored proposal worked to have the International Geophysical Year (IGY) body put out a call for satellite launches that year. The IGY body met in Rome during October of that year (1955).

While the US was simply working to increase recognition and worldwide acceptance of the use of satellites, this prepared the two superpowers for something that neither had anticipated.

The US Announces Its Intentions

Although nearly fifteen years had passed since the attack on Pearl Harbor, in 1955, Americans were still very much aware of the surprise attack and feared a similar attack as the tension of the Cold War worsened. After all, the Soviets had successfully stolen the knowledge of how to build a nuclear weapon and had managed to create their own. This was why the US had established the "Surprise Attack Panel" the Technological Capabilities Panel) responsible for generating the previously mentioned reports. To prevent another surprise attack, the US determined the best way to be aware of would-be attackers was to be able to literally spot the attackers long before they arrived in the US.

To alleviate the concerns of Americans, the US wanted to monitor the USSR territories. To establish this kind of regular surveillance as an acceptable practice, in US President Dwight D. Eisenhower proposed in 1955 that the US and USSR agree to allow flights over each other's territories. His proposal was called "Open Skies." Unsurprisingly, this idea was rejected by the USSR. Stalin had died in March of 1953, leaving the superpower to recover from the loss of a tyrant who often killed those closest to him as he became increasingly paranoid. His successor, Georgy Malenkov, took over the day Stalin died but had only lasted as the USSR leader until September of that same year. Nikita Khrushchev took over the day Malenkov was forced to leave office. Having been in office for less than two years, Khrushchev was moving away from some of the more extreme policies of Stalin's regime. Still, he did not want to appear to agree with the US on topics that might make the USSR seem weak. Rejecting a policy that would allow Americans to fly over its lands seemed like the thing to do.

Following the rejection of this policy, the US government decided it could accomplish longer-term surveillance at a lower cost by sending a satellite into space. The satellite would provide surveillance every time it went over Soviet lands. If the US could do this successfully, it would not be risking any American lives, since the satellite would be unmanned. Secondly, the USSR wouldn't be able to eliminate it since missiles were not powerful enough to reach space. And, even if they could, they were not sophisticated enough to accurately hit a target outside Earth's atmosphere.

Following the IGY body's approval of its satellite project in May of 1955, the US began to move on it. Having adopted a policy of relative openness and honesty about what it was doing, the US made the announcement on July 29, 1955. President Eisenhower spoke to Americans, telling them that the US was dedicated to creating a satellite that would help keep the country safe. He also asked for companies to start submitting proposals to create the satellite.

By making his announcement and calling for proposals, Eisenhower had started the Space Race. Knowing that the US was ardently working on a satellite, the USSR was quick to move forward with Korolev's proposal to use the ballistic missile to help launch a satellite of its own.

The USSR Responds

The US may have been the first to announce its intention to send a satellite into space, but the USSR was already ahead of the idea—its government had just not been as vocal or as focused on it. Korolev's proposal suddenly looked a lot more serious, and they were not about to lose the advantage his keen interest in space gave them. While the US was just starting to look for proposals, the USSR already had Korolev's ideas firmly established. This gave them a nearly two-year advantage.

The talks started internally at first, with Korolev presenting his satellite ideas to the Military-Industrial Commission in August of 1955. The commission soon approved his proposal to use one of its new launchers to send a satellite that weighed 1.5 tons into space. The decision was not unanimous, as there were several missile specialists who thought the focus on satellites would be a problem in the further development of ballistic missiles. Korolev had helped persuade many of the commission to agree by saying he would be able to launch before the start of the 1956 IGY. While there was buy-in for the program, the Soviet Council of Ministers was slow in its announcement, waiting for the early part of 1956 to officially authorize the program.

By the early part of 1956, both the world's superpowers were actively working to send a satellite into space, though the US had no idea just how far behind the USSR they were.

Chapter 4 – The USSR and USA Prepare Their Satellites and Their Sites

With the intentions of the two governments firmly established (whether those intentions were well known to other nations or not), the Space Race began. Now, both the USSR and US had much work ahead to accomplish what they said they wanted to do. The USSR believed they were already ahead with Korolev's work. By comparison, the US was still trying to come up with ideas for launching the satellite.

Both sides needed much more than just ideas and equipment to launch their respective efforts, however. They needed design plans, reliable personnel, and a large amount of space to test their progress. They also wanted to secure the test sites from both spies and the public, as they expected far more failed attempts than successful ones, especially in the early days.

IGY 1957 to 1958

IGY was an international program implemented to collect information and to research and study geophysics and the planetary environment of Earth. It included scientists from eleven major scientific fields, including gravity, ionospheric physics, and solar activity. While there was nothing to specifically aid in satellite development, several of the IGY fields touched on the technology that satellites either used or would benefit from their use.

The IGY was selected to run between 1957 and 1958 because the sunspot cycle would be at its zenith. This period had been established by an international group of geophysicists back in 1950. Its primary purpose was to act as a follow-up to the Second International Polar Year from 1932 to 1933. The initial focus on polar studies quickly widened to encompass eleven fields, as the geophysicists were interested in discussing the many advances in technology, including rocketry. When the International Council of Scientific Unions sanctioned the IGY, seventy nations began to assemble their own scientists to attend, and seventy nations participating in the program.

Both the US and the USSR used this meeting to their advantage. The participants in the IGY not only discussed the results of their studies but also got information from the successful launches of the satellites not long after the end of the IGY. For the two superpowers, it provided a way of learning more about each other's progress. As they worked through their plans, they used some of the information provided during the IGY to try to guess how far along the other country was toward meeting their common goal.

One thing both nations seemed to fail to realize was that their initial timelines were compromised as soon as they declared their intentions, whether publicly or from within their respective organizations, because of the amount of information their scientists did not know. The IGY proved to be a way of understanding more, and the international world eventually benefited from it far more than either of the two superpowers.

The Development of the R-7 and Object-D

Korolev had proposed his satellite to the Military-Industrial Commission back in the summer of 1955 with a timeline that would have resulted in the satellite being launched prior to the start of the IGY. Unfortunately, the delayed authorization put the plans behind schedule by several months. When it was finally approved, the satellite they were to launch was initially named Object-D. It would be developed at OKB-1 (Korolev's design bureau) along with the R-7 missile.

A month after the project was approved, Soviet Premier Nikita Khrushchev visited the site to see the progress being made on the R-7 missile. Realizing that it was a perfect opportunity to push the project along more quickly, Korolev took a mockup of his Object-D to show to the premier. To persuade him of the importance of the project, Korolev showed Khrushchev both the mockup and the plans he had regarding the US satellite. Like the missile specialists, Khrushchev was concerned that the satellite would adversely affect the missile program's progress. Korolev persuaded the premier of the project's value and that it would not interfere with the missile project. With this assurance, Khrushchev endorsed what soon became the most advanced space program of the time. It was Korolev's persistence that ultimately pushed the USSR to be the leader in the Space Race.

One of the reasons Korolev was successful in getting the premier's endorsement was that he showed that the R-7 intercontinental ballistic missile was already well along in the development process. Since they were planning to use the R-7 to launch their satellite, they were much further along than the US, which was opting to create an entirely different rocket for its efforts to get a satellite into space. Planning to use a model that was already in development enabled the USSR to work on both ballistic missiles and satellites at the same time.

Selecting a Proposal and Choosing a Site

Three primary proposals were considered by the US:

1. The US Air Force submitted what they called the "World Series plan." This plan included a satellite that weighed as much as 5,000 pounds, launched by an Atlas missile.

2. The Army submitted Project Orbiter, which included a satellite that was only five pounds and would be launched with a Redstone missile.

3. The Naval Research Laboratory submitted the Project Vanguard proposal, which had more capabilities than the Project Orbiter. Unlike the other two proposals, the Vanguard required the development of a new rocket to get it into the atmosphere; the new rocket would be based on the existing Viking sounding rocket.

The team reviewing the proposals quickly ruled out the US Air Force's proposal because they thought it posed a potential problem to missile development. It was harder for them to eliminate the Army's proposal because it was both further along (since they would not need to create a new rocket) and more cost-effective. However, the Vanguard offered a more in terms of scientific capability thanks to the wide range of instruments it included. This was far more aligned with the goals of the IGY. For a short period, the committee considered merging the two proposals, using the Vanguard satellite with the rocket proposed by the Army. Ultimately, the rivalry between the two branches of the US military led the committee to decide not to mix proposals. The two proposals were put to the vote, and the Vanguard was selected by a single vote. In August 1955, the US selected Project Vanguard to serve as a science satellite for the IGY.

On September 9, 1955, the US officially started the project, building six vehicles with the hope that one of them would be successful. With a budget of $20 million and eighteen months to complete the six vehicles, the US finally began to plan for its satellite launch.

Today, this decision is criticized because it put the US behind the USSR, though there was no way for the US to know that at the time. Had they gone with either of the other two proposals, the US would have been largely on equal footing with the USSR. One other important consideration at the time was to have the satellite appear to be a joint effort between the government and the private sector. The Vanguard met this criterion and helped create the image that the US was working toward an Open Skies precedent. The goal was to establish that private companies could have satellites flying over other nations without being considered a threat. If people associated satellites with governments, it would make the satellites seem more sinister and perhaps be less acceptable.

The US was working toward this goal when the USSR announced it would launch a satellite during the IGY. With many Americans seeing this as a potential threat, they quickly looked to the US government to ensure they were first. Unfortunately, the selection of the Vanguard almost guaranteed the US would be second, with far more to develop and test than the USSR did. It also had no use as a military tool since it did not rely on a ballistic missile to lift a heavy payload.

With both sides finally committed to their programs, it was just a matter of time before one of them was successful. They both had the necessary scientists, sites, and tools. Their approaches were significantly different, largely because they had very different assessments of each other. While the USSR was constantly monitoring the US for its progress, the US continued to assume its own superiority. The US had been the first to develop working nuclear weapons and had more advanced weapons, so it believed it would be the first nation to reach space. The USSR had made an announcement, but it was far more difficult to know its progress, considering it did not broadcast details, and its program was tightly locked behind military security. By comparison, the US government had plans that were more accessible, particularly as it was working with the private sector. This did not mean the Soviets were always accurate in their assessment of how far the US had progressed, but the Soviets did tend to overestimate the Americans, pushing them to act faster and to work longer hours to stay ahead. This eventually paid off in 1957.

Chapter 5 – Russian Accomplishes Several Firsts with Sputnik 1, 2, and 3

As the US felt comfortable it would be the first to successfully launch a satellite, Korolev became increasingly concerned the nation's confidence would be justified. To be the first to succeed, he faced the Presidium of the Soviet Academy of Sciences to request additional funds during September of 1956. He and his team were already behind schedule, and he saw the dream of being first slipping away. This fear was largely based on a report (which turned out to be incorrect) that said the US had tested a launch in Cape Canaveral earlier in the month. Though the report seems to have indicated the launch failed, the truth was that the US had not advanced that far quite yet.

Korolev's concerns were further compounded by issues the team was having with the R-7 engine. They had modified it so that it could launch a heavy satellite, but the engine's thrust levels were insufficient. Fearful of losing their advantage, Korolev began to drive his team to work longer hours to resolve the issues, but it became clear they needed to change their plans since they were too far behind schedule to meet their target launch date. Knowing they couldn't possibly succeed, Korolev finally adjusted the plan.

At the beginning of 1957, the team reduced the weight of the satellite to reduce the amount of power and thrust needed to get the satellite into the atmosphere. Still believing in the report that said the US was already testing rockets, Korolev got approval for the changes. At the time, he was concerned the US would be successful within the next few months, a fear that was unfounded.

New Satellites

Not sure how much time he had before the US would be successful, Korolev tried to come up with a solution that would work better with their current progress. This resulted in two simpler satellites called the PS-1 and PS-2, which were only about 220 pounds each. PS was short for *prosteishy sputnik*, which translates "simplest satellite," indicating that they were switching to a simpler version to ensure they beat the US into space. This change required approval to proceed, which was finally given by the Soviet Council of Ministers in the middle of February 1957.

When the IGY started at the beginning of July 1957, the Soviets were testing their work. The US Central Intelligence Agency (CIA) had learned of their progress and was trying to warn the Eisenhower administration without rousing too much concern. Korolev likely did not know that the US was far behind his work, which worked in his favor because it helped to drive him to try to finish the work before the US. His drive ensured that the USSR would be first in getting an artificial satellite into space. He and his team suffered three failures by the end of July, and not until August did they finally have a successful test of the R-7.

Once it had a successful test, the Soviet Union decided to announce its progress to the world. This announcement was met with skepticism in the US, and the USSR continued to make progress without the US feeling driven to beat them. When the USSR successfully launched the R-7 a second time in the early part of September, it didn't celebrate with nearly as much fanfare: it had already been the first nation to successfully test an intercontinental ballistic missile. Whatever the reaction from the US, there was no need to make a stir again. The Soviet Union was more interested in being successful at the next stage—getting a satellite into space.

The USSR had initially targeted September 17 as the date to accomplish this, but with several failures over the summer and the second successful launch on September 7, the target date was adjusted so they could ensure any issues were worked out prior to launching a satellite. A new date was approved: October 6, 1957. Paranoid that the US was making advances faster than it was admitting, or perhaps in response to the USSR's successes, Korolev had the date moved to October 4. They had to make further modifications to the R-7 with the lighter satellites.

Having created two smaller, modified satellites, Korolev's team planned to use PS-1 for the October 4 launch. With everything apparently ready, the USSR prepared to become the first nation to send an artificial object into Earth's atmosphere.

Sputnik 1

The PS-1 was silver and round with four antennas that extended from the core of the satellite. It was roughly twenty-two inches around and looked fairly innocuous. The core of the satellite was about the size of a basketball, but with the four antennae, it ended up being bigger than a person. The outside was made from an aluminum alloy. The most threatening-looking part of it was the radio beacon that flashed as it pinpointed different places on the planet's surface.

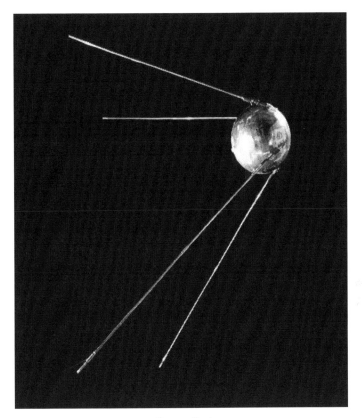

Sputnik 1
(https://live.staticflickr.com/8041/8052668653_4c784d13f6_z.jpg)

Since Sputnik was not the original satellite, its abilities and lifespan were greatly reduced. It was considered an elementary satellite. With its reduced capacity, its primary purpose was to simply add radio transmitters into Earth's orbit. The USSR had already learned about the need to protect against heat, so the outside included a heat shield sphere. The next layer of the satellite was a pressurized sphere to protect the silver-zinc batteries and radio transmitters inside, which created a beeping noise.

On October 3, Korolev and his team began to prepare for the launch. The modified R-7 was moved onto what they planned to use as the launchpad for the first and future launches. The R-7 spaceport has come to be known as the Baikonur Cosmodrome, and it was developed by Korolev's friend Tikhonravov. The R-7 rocket that was originally planned had been changed so much that it was given a new designation, 8K71PS. Much of what was included on the R-7 was removed for the model to launch the PS-1, including the military warhead, hardware designed to measure launch data, a considerable amount of avionics to monitor vibration, and the radio control system.. Since they had switched to a less robust satellite, much of the planned tracking system originally established for Object D was not in place for the launch of the PS-1. Only the necessary systems were ready by the launch. In February 1957, they had established the radio transmitter specifications, and those were verified before the launch.

Once the equipment was set up, the Russian team began to fuel the rocket at 5:45 a.m. Sixteen hours passed before everything was ready and the R-7 launched the PS-1 into space. Six minutes after the rocket launched, it ejected the PS-1 into the atmosphere. At some point, the satellite received a new name, Sputnik, which roughly translates to "traveling companion" or "fellow traveler" depending on the translator. It would come to be known as *Sputnik 1*. Today, the term *sputnik* is often synonymous with the term satellite, showing just how important this remarkable accomplishment was.

At night, the satellite could be seen orbiting the Earth. It took less than one hundred minutes for Sputnik to fully travel around the world. Even on cloudy nights, it could sometimes be seen as it passed overhead, the beeping from the radio transmitters helping observers pinpoint its location. During its time in orbit, it had five specific objectives:

- Test the method of launching a satellite into orbit

- Calculate the lifetime of the satellite in orbit to determine the atmosphere's density

- Try both the radio and optical functions placed in the satellite

- Test radio wave propagation for satellites in the Earth's atmosphere

- Check the pressurization principles on the satellite

As soon as the satellite began to orbit the Earth, Soviet news began to broadcast information about the successful launch. This could have been premature since the satellite had not yet fully orbited. Still, even if it had not fully orbited the Earth, it was the first artificial object in space. Flight controllers detected the Tral telemetry system operating in the satellite as *Sputnik 1* made its second revolution. Both the satellite and the rocket booster reached lower-Earth orbit.

Korolev's role in this accomplishment is undeniable, as he was the one who kept pushing for the USSR to strive for space instead of focusing solely on developing weapons. However, his friend Tikhonravov was responsible for much of the project's successes. Having been a member of GIRD, one of the early Soviet rocket research organizations, Tikhonravov had extensive knowledge about missiles and participated in numerous studies into what was necessary to orbit the planet. Both these figures receive most of the credit for what was accomplished with Sputnik, and they continued to play key roles over the course of the Space Race. Several other notable figures included Mstislav Vsevolodovich Keldysh and Dmitry Fedorovich Ustinov. Keldysh, a scientist who was a strong proponent of developing calculations and mathematical solutions to space flight, was instrumental to the success of Sputnik. Ustinov, who came from a working-class family, became the Deputy Chairman of the Soviet of Ministers, and his dedication and political support helped ensure *Sputnik* had the resources necessary to succeed. Without these two figures, Tikhonravov and Korolev alone may not have ensured that the USSR achieved the distinction of the first nation to reach space.

The batteries at the core of *Sputnik 1* were not made to last, and after just twenty-two days, they died. *Sputnik 1* continued to circle the Earth for a few more months (staying in orbit for roughly three months) before falling back to Earth. It had only reached the lower part of Earth's orbit, so it was not going to remain in orbit for long. On January 4, 1958, Sputnik finally began to fall back to Earth, burning up as it re-entered the atmosphere.

Sputnik 2

Following the rousing success of *Sputnik 1* and the lack of response from the US (at least in terms of establishing its own success), the Soviet Union continued to press to achieve other firsts. While *Sputnik 1* was no longer sending signals, it was still orbiting the Earth when *Sputnik 2* was prepared. This time, the USSR was determined to send a living creature into space. On November 3, 1957, the Soviets prepared *Sputnik 2*, which weighed more than 1,100 pounds so that it could protect the living creature—a dog named Laika. The date was selected by Khrushchev, who wanted to mark the 40th anniversary of the Bolshevik Revolution that had removed the Russian monarch and ushered in Communism.

The history of animals in space pre-dates the Space Race. Fruit flies were the first living organisms to reach space and then return when the US launched them on a V-2 rocket in 1947. In 1950, a mouse was shot into space and died. This initial failure was followed by a few successful attempts where the rockets that housed the animals were robust enough that the protection didn't disintegrate. Since the exterior was strong enough to handle reentry, the parachutes were fully functional when they needed to deploy. The first monkey, named Albert II, was launched into space in 1949 and safely returned with the use of a parachute. His predecessor and two successors all died when the rockets carrying them failed.

The reason Laika's launch received so much attention was that she would not be immediately returning to Earth. Laika was a stray mutt (a mix between a spitz and a husky) taken off the streets of Moscow to become the first living creature to go to space. She was chosen from a group of other stray female dogs after passing a series of tests that sought the most docile and obedient dog from the group. The potential dogs were tested to see how they would react to loud noises and changes in air pressure, as the dog would experience these during the initial launch. A little dog named Kudryavka, or Little Curly, was selected because of her placid nature and how well she reacted to the changes. A back-up dog named Albina was chosen, as well. The public saw Kudryavka as the Soviet news introduced her to the people. She barked a lot during her time on air, gaining her the name Laika, or "barker." Both Laika and Albina had small medical devices implanted into their bodies so that their heart rate, blood pressure, breathing pattern, and movements could be monitored.

When it was time to start preparing for the launch, Laika was put into her own little specially-designed spacesuit, which was meant to keep any waste from damaging the instruments onboard. The launch occurred at 5:30 a.m. on November 3, 1957, and it had a G-force that measured five times higher than the usual pull of gravity. The Soviets monitored Laika, and her vital signs showed that she was frightened by the launch, with her heart rate tripling.

They did not plan for the dog's safe re-entry, though. Given only one meal and enough oxygen to last for seven days, the unfortunate Laika died while orbiting the planet. They could not offer more meals to the dog because it would have put the satellite over the payload the rocket could manage. One physician was said to have felt bad, and despite the protocols, she gave Laika a meal prior to lift off to help the dog survive as long as possible.

Though they knew that Laika would not survive, they had thought she would survive for at least seven days. Had she lived long enough for the oxygen to be used up, it was thought she would die a painless death about fifteen seconds later. However, it wasn't the loss of oxygen that killed her. The USSR did not realize what kind of temperatures she would encounter once she was in orbit. Her vital signs showed that she did reach orbit, but she did not survive long after that. About 103 minutes after launch, Laika entered orbit. She had a rapid increase in temperature, which meant she had lost her heat shield. By the time the capsule was making its fourth revolution, the temperature inside was more than ninety degrees, and they don't think she was alive much longer than that as the temperature continued to rise.

Sputnik 2 was in orbit for a few months longer than the first satellite. It is said the Soviet Union falsified the documents to make it sound like Laika survived for days after the launch instead of the few hours she likely experienced. An initial belief was that she could be brought back safely, but the Soviets admitted she died after *Sputnik 2* had been in orbit for nine days.

This event became one of the first major points of contention in the Space Race. Though animal rights weren't nearly as well established as they are today, there was an outcry from many nations about the Soviet's plan to send a dog into space without any intention of returning the dog safely back to Earth. Her fate has received a lot more attention in recent history, and the dog has received attention in different forms of media.

What the world learned about space during Laika's short time in space was that life could be sustained with proper planning and care. The biggest obstacle to the trip was the return, which generated unimaginable heat that destroyed the early Soviet satellites. Ironically, she was not the first dog to reach space, though. The Soviets had adjusted German V-2 rockets following the end of World War II that sent dogs into space, then parachuted them back to the planet. However, Laika was the first to spend more than a few fleeting moments in space as she orbited Earth.

Sputnik 3

Following two successful launches that firmly established the USSR as the dominant nation in space travel, the push to do more was temporarily alleviated. With his schedule largely all his own, Korolev returned to focusing on Object-D. Following the events of the last two launches, he decided to make two of them.

The originally planned satellite, Object-D, was finally completed by the beginning of 1958. By this time, the US had finally reached space, but the USSR was still well ahead, having sent a living creature to space (though they failed to sustain life). With those two successes, Object-D was finally prepared for launch, and it was named *Sputnik 3*. This satellite was more specific and ambitious than the stripped-down satellites launched as *Sputnik 1* and *Sputnik 2*.

In April of 1958, the USSR began preparing to launch Object-D into space. On April 27, they completed the launch of the much heavier satellite. For the first time, one of their planned launches did not go as planned, and the rocket with the Object-D failed to reach orbit. Less than two minutes after launch, the team watched the rocket disintegrate and crash back to the ground. The team went to check the crash site and were surprised to find that the satellite had not been destroyed by the fire and subsequent crash. As they returned with it to the facility, it began to short circuit, starting a fire that nearly destroyed the satellite. Given the number of problems with the first one, Korolev decided to use the backup satellite.

A new launch date was set for May 15, 1958, and this time, the launch was virtually flawless. By this time, the US had launched more satellites into space than the USSR, but the satellites were not as advanced as *Sputnik 3*.

Sputnik 3 had a recorder that failed to work properly, which meant it was not able to complete all the planned objectives. At nearly 3,000 pounds, it was the heaviest satellite to reach space. While the recorder did not work as intended, the twelve instruments on board provided data on a range of Earth measurements, including the upper atmosphere, radiation, cosmic dust, and the Earth's magnetic fields. The other instruments worked, though the data was not able to be recorded.

In April of 1960, *Sputnik 3* finally returned to Earth.

Chapter 6 – Americans Play Catchup

The reports that had lit a fire under Korolev and driven him to expedite his plans so late in the game were gravely mistaken. Just as he and his team were finding significant problems with their work, the US was experiencing its own problems as it worked to build both a satellite and a new rocket to get the satellite into space. Also like Korolev, the US team had to request more money to make changes and adjustments based on what they found when they tried to put their ideas into practice.

As the cost of the Vanguard development and testing increased, the program faced the threat of reduction (though it wasn't at much risk of cancellation). Only when the US was forced to realize it was not leading the world did it feel a similar motivation to catch up to the Soviet's success.

A Problem of Budget

The original of $20 million ballooned into a $110 million effort, and people within the scientific community began to question if the program was worth the price tag. After all, the US still believed it would be the first to launch a satellite into space, and there were no reliable reports to indicate it had any reason to be concerned about the USSR's progress. A memorandum about the unexpected costs was sent to the president to address the issue.

Despite the budget issue, the US was finding successes in its testing by May 1957. The team pointed to these successes as proof that the ballooning costs were worth the effort because they had gone from the planning stages in the fall of 1955 to testing by the spring of 1957. John Hagan, Vanguard's program director, also pointed out that the success of the program would offer a wealth of scientific benefits, the declared reason the US was dedicating so many resources to the effort. To play on Eisenhower's idea of what was possible for the future, the director pointed to the way the achievement would greatly benefit the scientific community and change the direction of the world as people realized that space was achievable. Unfortunately for Hagen, Eisenhower was far more interested in the project's costs and did not let them continue to balloon regardless of the possible benefits. The president accused the team of creating satellites that he had not approved. He also said that the prestige would come from the success of the launch, not the instruments that would provide scientific readings. The primary reason Eisenhower was willing to let the program continue was that the US had announced it would launch a satellite. Americans were excited and expectant, and the global community and the IGY had been told that the US would go through with it. This led Eisenhower to believe it was necessary to put money into the program, but he was beginning to think it wasn't the progressive program he once thought it was.

Since he had little interest in seeing the progress of the program that was becoming increasingly expensive, he didn't think it was necessary to complete all six of the satellites since the program would achieve its goal as soon as one of them was successfully launched. He felt no urgency because the US was still confident that no one else was anywhere close to achieving its goals. However, they were well behind the USSR by this point, as Korolev and his team were preparing to test (if not already testing).

During the early part of July 1957, the CIA reported that the USSR was making progress much faster than the US had expected. Based on what it had learned, it seemed possible the Soviets would successfully launch a satellite by the middle of September, around the anniversary of Russian rocket pioneer Konstantin Tsiolkovsky's birthday. The CIA informed both the Deputy Secretary of Defense and Eisenhower's administration. The news was largely brushed off with the idea that it could be a false report to get them to spend more money.

That all changed on October 4, 1957, with the announcement that the USSR had more than successfully tested a satellite. *Sputnik 1* was more than just a known threat—it could be seen tearing across the skies in the US on a clear night. The paranoia that came with this sight caused the US to ramp up its efforts as the Americans found themselves slipping from an assumed comfortable lead to a distant second to the USSR. This was a concern not only because of the implications that the USSR could monitor the US but also because it showed that US military and science superiority was not as secure as most people thought.

With *Sputnik 1* traveling over the US about seven times a day, the American people wanted to know what the US government was doing to protect them. This question was slightly louder than the demands to know how the USSR managed to beat the US into space.

Soothing the Concern

The first problem with the Soviet's success was not an indication of a technological failing; it was the reaction of the American people. After all its modifications, *Sputnik 1* was about 185 pounds, which was far heavier than the Vanguard that the US was developing. As impressive as the vision of *Sputnik 1* was, it inspired a sense of dread. The US was not the first nation to reach space, and there was also fear that the

USSR would initiate a surprise attack. The events since the tragic day at Pearl Harbor less than two decades earlier were still very fresh on the minds of the American people. While there was no physical war being fought, Americans questioned just what was happening with the project that had been announced back in 1955. The US had been the first to announce its intentions, yet the Soviets had managed to beat them into space. If the Soviets could launch a heavy satellite into space, they had the necessary technology to launch a ballistic missile at the US. Since the USSR had successfully tested their own nuclear bombs, the threat was even greater.

Having devalued the project and ignored the indications that the Soviets were nearing success, Eisenhower and his administration were forced to face their own failings and lack of vision. The unexpected success by the Soviets, something that they had been warned about months before it happened, was a wakeup call that made the US start to take the Vanguard project far more seriously.

As *Sputnik 1* passed over the US, unnerving Americans, Eisenhower tried to downplay what it meant. Having already expressed his displeasure at the cost of the Vanguard project, he was soon forced to realize the mistake he and his administration had made. Instead of leading the world into space, the US was playing catchup to the USSR.

The US suddenly had a reason to make space exploration their top priority, and soon, money was flowing into the Vanguard program.

A New Drive to Succeed

Although Eisenhower insisted there was nothing to fear, reports on the progress of the Vanguard began broadcasting to the American people. US scientists were working on not only the Vanguard rocket but also a satellite called the *Explorer 1* that would be launched into space. Live reports were given to help to show the people that the US was not far behind the Soviets. Unfortunately, the reporters ended up broadcasting just how far behind the US was when they inadvertently broadcasted the explosion of the Vanguard to American homes.

It was a horrible setback. As the news came up with clever headlines like "Kaputnik," the officials decided that they would need to change their approach. As they discussed what to do, they decided to switch to the Juno rocket. They also decided to work in secret, more like the USSR had done, to ensure there weren't any more public embarrassments that would reduce the people's trust in what the US could accomplish. They had managed to retrieve the satellite, but it was damaged because of the explosion of the rocket.

Now working in secret at Cape Canaveral, the team moved forward with the launch. When they felt that they were nearly ready, they let the media know that they were preparing to try again. Fully aware that the USSR had managed to launch two satellites into space, including the ill-fated journey of Laika, the US prepared for its second attempt to launch a satellite into space. The team was ready on January 31, 1958, but instead of using the Vanguard again, it used the rocket that the US Army had suggested, one that had been worked on by von Braun and his team. The new rocket was called the Jupiter-C. At the same time, Jet Propulsion Laboratory had been designing and building the satellite, which they completed within three months.

The US successfully launched its first satellite into space on January 31, 1958. Since the primary purpose for the satellite wasn't military use, the satellite worked to learn more about space. *Explorer 1* was more than just a satellite; it was a cosmic ray detector. As it orbited, it measured the radiation around Earth. Scientists were surprised to find that the count was lower than they had expected. The measurements and results were run by Dr. James Van Allen. Based on findings, he began to theorize there was a belt of radiation around the Earth, a theory that was confirmed by the second US satellite. The US may not have been the first to reach space, but it was the first to transmit signals back from space. *Explorer 1* also provided scientific data that helped scientists better understand the area around the Earth's atmosphere. Repeated trips into space found that the radiation belt trapped radiation, and the belts were called the Van Allen Radiation Belts in honor of the project leader. Both the USSR and US would have to take this finding into account later as they sought to send people further away from Earth. At this time, the US was behind the USSR in what they had accomplished, but they were collecting data that would give them a distinct advantage later. While the USSR focused on accomplishing as much as possible as quickly as possible, the US was trying to learn from each mission. The US met many of the same goals a bit behind their Soviet counterparts because they were also gathering data. They also had an advantage because they were working with other nations who were interested in space travel but were still recovering from the devastation of World War II. This desire to collaborate would further slow the US in the beginning, but it would significantly boost its abilities to accomplish feats at a steady pace.

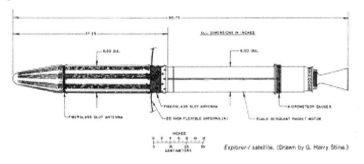

Explorer 1 (https://upload.wikimedia.org/wikipedia/commons/f/f0/ Explorer1_sketch.jpg)

While slower to reach space, the US sent *Explorer 1* higher than the *Sputnik*s had gone. Since *Explorer 1* was higher, it orbited the Earth every 115 minutes, with fewer than thirteen orbits each day. It began to transmit information back to Earth on May 23, 1958, and fell back to Earth more than twelve years later on March 31, 1970, having lasted far longer than any of the first *Sputnik*s. It was able to remain in space longer because it had gone so much higher over the planet.

A launch of *Explorer 2* was attempted on March 5, 1958, but it failed. Unlike the first failed launch attempt, this time the problem was that the Jupiter-C rocket's phases did not function as expected. The US's next attempt to send *Explorer 3* into space was successful on March 26, 1958. It continued to function until June 16, 1958.

Between the failed launch of *Explorer 2* and the successful launch of *Explorer 3*, the US mirrored the progress of the USSR. After abandoning its original satellite in favor of something more certain, the US returned to its original satellite for the third launch. On March 17, less than two weeks after the failed attempt to launch *Explorer 2*, the US successfully sent *Vanguard 1* into space. Well ahead of its time, *Vanguard 1* was solar-powered. This satellite could better study the shape of the Earth and reported back that it was asymmetrical, more closely resembling a pear than a ball. This satellite also has the distinction of being the oldest satellite in space, as it is still orbiting the Earth as of 2020. However, it stopped transmitting back in 1964.

By this point, the US had sent one more satellite into space than the USSR and had obtained data from its satellites. However, the US had not managed to create anything that could support life to reach space. This gave each side different advantages, although the US was far more open (while not necessarily more honest) about what it achieved. After its very public early failures, the US was no more eager to discuss its failures than the USSR was. Still, there were a few televised failures since the US continued to broadcast many of the launches.

The US successfully launched *Explorer 4* on July 26, 1958, a few months after *Sputnik 3*. Then the launch of *Explorer 5* failed, showing that both the US and USSR were still trying to find their footing. There remained as many failures as successes since little was known about space when the Space Race began. The failures also showed that both needed to move more carefully as they sought to be the first to reach the ultimate goal of sustaining life in space and returning that life safely.

The Formation of the National Aeronautics and Space Administration

With the launch of *Sputnik 3*, the US decided that its approach to coordinating and managing space exploration simply wasn't working—it was again falling behind. A Congressional hearing was held to create an agency with the sole purpose of running the American space program. Like the efforts up to that point, the dedicated agency would be a civilian agency, not a military one (something that is still true today). The creation of the National Aeronautics and Space Administration (NASA) was approved by Congress through the *National Aeronautics and Space Act* in July 1958. Eisenhower signed the act into law roughly a month later, and NASA officially began to operate at the beginning of October 1958. By the time the high-tech *Sputnik 3* fell out of orbit in 1960, NASA was helping to close the gap between the two superpowers.

NASA was intended to prove that the US was not just developing ballistic weaponry; it was serious about scientific findings. Therefore, a second agency attached to the military was started to keep ballistic weaponry separate from space development. Called the Advanced Research Projects Agency, it also began operating in 1958.

Chapter 7 – Different Approaches to Getting the First Men in Space

The IGY was as exciting and busy as the two superpowers had promised. Between 1957 and 1958, they had both made significant strides toward space exploration. However, the technology used to launch the satellites into space was based on weaponry. The US and USSR achieved their rockets so quickly because they used the knowledge of German scientists, who had been close to completing ballistic missiles when World War II ended. Using this technology enabled the two superpowers to significantly reduce the time it took to start launching rockets and satellites.

As the USSR had found, rocket-launching technology was not ideal when dealing with living creatures. The ultimate goal was to achieve space travel, and getting a person into space was only the first challenge of many. They had expected Laika to last much longer than she did, but they had not known about the heat in Earth's atmosphere. Later, the two nations would learn that, away from Earth, temperatures were deadly cold. There was a lot to learn, but the final question was how to get people safely back from space. After the backlash from intentionally launching a dog into space knowing that she would not survive, neither nation was willing to risk sending people into space without a plan to bring them back safely. Figuring out how to achieve this would take them a while longer, and they continued launching different satellites to conduct tests.

The Studies, Failures, and Accomplishments of the Soviet Union

Between 1957 and 1961, both the US and USSR divided their time and resources between developing a way of launching a person into space and safely returning them and continued work on satellites. The US was dedicated to making satellites as scientifically beneficial as possible, while the USSR was more focused on travel.

After their two successful launches in 1957, the USSR only launched one satellite in 1958. *Sputnik 3* was a significant success, but it was not their only attempt to launch more satellites into space. During 1958, the Soviets had only attempted to send two satellites into space—the initial failed launch of *Sputnik 3* and then its success. Following *Sputnik 3*'s successful launch on May 15, the USSR did not attempt another launch until January 1959. They attempted to send *Luna 1* on January 2, which was a partial success. It was the first artificial craft to make it to the moon, marking the beginning of a series of crafts that the USSR would launch toward the moon. *Luna 1* would reach the moon, but instead of landing on the moon, the satellite shot past it. Since it did not have any propulsion system of its own, this could not be corrected. As it moved away from Earth, the orange glow of the trail left by the craft could be seen back on Earth. *Luna 1* was not only the first satellite to go close to the moon but also the first craft to have left Earth's orbit. It was pulled into orbit around the sun after losing contact with the USSR about sixty-two hours after it was launched. Today, *Luna 1* is circling the sun, taking about 450 days to complete a full orbit. However, it is small, making it nearly impossible to track with no signal.

Luna 1 (https://earthsky.org/upl/2012/12/luna-1.jpg)

The Soviet Union would successfully launch two more satellites as a part of the Luna satellite series in 1959. *Luna 2* was the first artificial object to land on the moon, and *Luna 3* successfully returned pictures of the dark side of the moon (the side that we cannot see on Earth).

In 1960, the Soviet Union continued its successful launches, making just two that year. However, the Soviets managed to achieve another major first on August 19, 1960, when they launched *Sputnik 5* into space. This was something that worked toward their longer-term goal of successfully getting a person into space and then back home. Instead of sending just one animal, though, they had what seems more of a menagerie aboard *Sputnik 5*. The passengers on this trip included fruit flies, a rabbit, a pair of rats, forty mice, and plants. However, it was the pair of dogs—named Belka and Strelka—that received the most attention, particularly when they returned to Earth safely. This launch was more like a test run for what was to come, and it was the last major launch before the Soviets moved onto the next major goal—launching a person into space and returning that person safely back to the ground.

Over time, Belka and Strelka became pop culture icons, inspiring music, cartoons (they were the inspiration for the 1990s cartoon *Ren & Stimpy*), and movies. Strelka had a puppy that was given to Khrushchev, who then gifted the dog to the US First Lady Jacqueline Kennedy. While there was a rivalry between the two nations, the US was the only other country that could understand the pressures of the Space Race, creating strong respect between the two nations that largely directed the path of humanity for several decades. Among many tense exchanges and the Cold War nearing the brink of nuclear war on several occasions, these friendly gestures helped improve the relationship between the two superpowers and set the rest of the world at ease.

The Studies, Failures, and Accomplishments of the US

The US was working toward getting a man into space, but it was also diligent about conducting scientific experiments. From the early days of the agency, it had stated its dedication to launching a pilot into orbit in as short a time as was possible. However, over 1958, the US would have more failed attempts than successes, showing the nation had a long road before it could consider launching a person safely into space. In 1959, US satellites continued to focus on furthering science, even as the Soviet Union continued to collect a string of firsts. Perhaps the constant drive to achieve more came at the cost of getting things right. As the USSR was in a position to be the leader, it had more time, which could have caused the US to push when it wasn't necessarily ready. However, each of these failures provided valuable lessons that the US used to improve its devices and technology.

With a heavy focus on studying space, the US was gaining details about space that would help it create a more reliable rocket.

Other Nations Join in the Race

The Space Race usually refers to the competition between the USSR and the US, but other nations began to join them in sending satellites into space during the 1960s. The UK sent its first satellite into space on April 26th, 1962. The primary objective for its satellite was to gain more data about the relationships of the ionosphere and sun-ionosphere. Canada sent its first satellite, *Alouette* (skylark), into space on September 29, 1962. It was the first satellite to be built by a nation other than the two superpowers. Its primary purpose was also to study the ionosphere. Both the UK and Canada had responded to the US invitation (or more accurately, NASA's invitation) to join an international collaboration to learn about space. Joining the collaboration enabled both nations to use American rockets so that they did not have to develop their own, which the US and USSR had already shown was far more difficult than often anticipated.

Italy joined the collaboration in 1964, and France in 1965, both with their own successful satellites. Australia would send its first satellite from Australia in 1967 with the use of a US rocket. Nations would continue to collaborate, sending their own satellites into space. The decade would close with West Germany finally joining with its own satellite—and a much wider goal than that of previous satellites.

Chapter 8 – The First Men in Space

After spending several years testing in space and learning as much as possible with scientific instruments and short trips using animals, both sides were getting closer to achieve one of the greatest accomplishments in human history—the successful launch of a person into—and back from—space. Both superpowers were eager to be the first, though they went about it in different ways.

The USSR would just barely beat the US to this milestone, with both hitting this goal in 1961.

Yuri Gagarin and a Question of What Counted as a Success

As its technology continued to advance, the Soviet Union started to review potential candidates for the first person in space. The Soviets had narrowed down their options to twenty potential candidates, whom they called cosmonauts. Each of the candidates was required to complete a series of tests to determine their ability to withstand the potential risks. The tests were once described by Cathleen Lewis: "They were performing enormous feats of physical training ... They wanted to test the limits of their pilots." The Soviets had learned from the other missions with animals that it was nearly impossible to guess what would happen once the launch began.

Two men stood out from the other candidates. Twenty-seven-year-old Yuri Gagarin was chosen to be the first Soviet (and, they hoped, person) in space, and Gherman Titov would be his backup. Reportedly, Gagarin had more humble origins, and this was desirable considering what they hoped he would become if the mission was successful. Titov had been raised in a family that was considered middle-class, while Gagarin's parents had been closer to blue-collar workers. This meant he had to overcome more to gain his place, which better represented what the Soviets wanted to portray—a person overcoming much longer odds to become a national hero. It would help inspire people across the Soviet Union to strive for more by working harder.

His humble background could have been a reason, but many people say it was more likely Gagarin's performance during the tests that ultimately led to his being chosen. Unaware that the US had been tracking its own countdown to launch someone into space, the Soviets pushed forward with its own plans in secret. Despite not knowing the American plans, the Soviets were aware that the US was making advances, and they were worried that they would lose the edge they had established through the first round of milestones. To ensure they were the first, the Soviets continued to push for a launch as soon as possible.

Following the rigorous selection process and testing, the USSR began to prepare for the launch, setting up *Vostok 1* on the launchpad. On April 12, 1961, Gagarin prepared himself at the top of a thirty-meter-high booster on the launch site in Kazakhstan (the modern-day Baikonur Cosmodrome). The cosmonaut was five-foot-two-inches tall, which made him a much better choice for the small quarters. Still, it couldn't have been terribly comfortable, as the rocket began to shake before departing from Earth. At 9:07 a.m., he uttered,

"Poyekhali," or "Here we go," as the rocket roared to life and launched him into the air.

Previous launches with animals had not told the Soviets what happened once the animals were in space. It was possible that the force of leaving Earth could cause him to lose consciousness. Because of this, they planned for mission control to assume control over the capsule. If he was awake as he orbited the Earth, Gagarin was given tubes with food that he could eat. There was also a ten-day supply of provisions in the event that something went wrong and the mission went longer than the single orbit that was planned. He was also able to relay his current experience back to ground control. The existing transcript from the mission had him reporting back how beautiful the Earth looked as he viewed it from the window of the little capsule. He could see how the shadows cast by clouds appeared from above the clouds. During this time, he was weightless, so Gagarin was also able to report back how he felt, proving that zero-g did not have any obvious adverse effect on a person's cognitive abilities.

A serious risk that was considered prior to his departure was what would happen if he were to lose contact with ground control, and with it, control of the vessel. To address this, NASA provided codes that would allow the cosmonaut to take control should he be disconnected. The capsule included a very crude computer that would allow him to maneuver the vessel.

Following the successful launch, Gagarin and the *Vostok 1* spent 108 minutes orbiting the Earth. They passed once around the planet, roughly 203 miles above the surface. Control then moved the vessel into what was likely a scary descent back to the ground. It is thought in such a controlled fall from space, the pull of gravity Gagarin likely felt was eight times greater than what we experience on the surface. His landing was completely up to the people controlling the vessel, and their control was minimal at best. He was in free fall until he was roughly four miles above the Earth. Then, he ejected from the capsule and parachuted back to the ground.

Some people have questioned whether the record is valid because Gagarin could not land his craft. This is based on the definition of success established by the Fédération Aéronautique Internationale (FAI), which has been the regulatory federation for air sports since 1905. The definition for a successful space flight was based on their regulations from aviation, which stated that the pilot must be able to land the ship. The USSR had not established a reliable way of braking upon reentry (they already had so many other variables to work with that this was not nearly as important). The Vostok craft had no braking mechanism since it was essentially a ballistic craft and followed the same kind of trajectory. Gagarin was ejected because there was no way for him to land safely at the speeds the craft was going. When Gherman Titov became the second person in space, he admitted that he had been ejected from his craft. Up to this point, it was thought that Gagarin had landed his craft, so this information started another controversy. Ultimately, the FAI had to recognize that there was an extremely different set of requirements for space travel than for regular flying. The speed, weight, and other elements of space travel meant that it needed a different definition of what was considered a success. It wasn't the landing that mattered. The fact remains that Gagarin was the first person to go into space and return to Earth to talk about his experience.

Following this success, Gagarin became one of the most notable heroes of the USSR. In March 1958, Gagarin and another pilot died while testing a new fighter jet. Though he did not live long after this first successful mission, he is still honored by people in Russian today, and his reputation wasn't restricted to the USSR. His face and name were plastered on newspapers across the world as the first person to ever enter space, and he lived to tell people just what he saw during his brief visit. When *Apollo 11* landed on the moon in 1969, the crew left a commemorative medallion for Gagarin, even though he did not die during a space mission. It was impossible to overstate just how important this first mission was. The *Apollo 11* crew also left medallions for others who had died in the pursuit of furthering space exploration.

Alan Shepard

Soon after NASA formed, they issued an invitation to 110 test pilots to become volunteers for the new spaceflight program. Alan Shepard was one of those original 110 pilots, but his invitation had gone astray, so he did not receive it. NASA managed to let him know, and he became one of the first seven men to become astronauts. From this group, Shepard was selected to be what NASA hoped would be the first person in space. His backup was John Glenn.

Project Mercury was meant to get the first person into space, and NASA spent several missions running tests with unmanned craft. On April 15, 1961, NASA and the US learned of the successful flight of Yuri Gagarin and realized they had missed their milestone. At best, Alan Shepard would be the first American in space and the second human to reach space. The US was incredibly close to having reached this milestone, so this was a blow to their hopes. The weather would further hinder their progress as the launch of *Mercury 7* was postponed from May 2nd due to weather conditions. It was again postponed because of the weather. On May 5, 1961 (less than a month after the Soviet's success), *Mercury 7* launched with Shepard aboard. After reaching 116 miles above the Earth's surface, Shepard remained in space for fifteen minutes. He did not get a chance to feel weightlessness because NASA had designed the craft so that he was strapped in too tightly to float. He also wasn't able to see the beauty of space because of where the porthole was located. Shepard did have a periscope so he could look outside, but it had a filter that made everything outside look black and white, including Earth.

While the Soviets had achieved the first human flight into space and a full orbit of the planet, *Mercury 7*'s flight gained attention because NASA was so open about its programs. Shepard's launch was televised to the world, and his return to Earth was also broadcasted live. Everyone knew that Gagarin had been the first person in space, but Shepard became a more easily identifiable space traveler because millions saw his trip. This created a connection with him that was not present with Gagarin. In fact, very little about what Gagarin experienced was detailed beyond the fact that he had successfully gone into space and returned.

Upon his return, Shepard was awarded the NASA Distinguished Service Medal, presented by President Kennedy. For the next few Mercury missions, Shepard continued to train, with his next planned flight on *Mercury 10*. However, this mission was scrapped following the successful full-day orbit by Gordon Cooper. Believing they didn't need to continue to test how people reacted to being in space, NASA switched over to the next phase, Project Gemini.

Shepard was designated to be one of the members of the first manned Gemini craft, but during training, he started to feel ill. Off-balance, dizzy, and nauseated, he reported to the physician. He was tested and diagnosed with Ménière's disease, which causes a buildup of fluid in the inner ear. Following the diagnosis, he was grounded from any solo jet test flights and told he could not go into space in 1963. For the next few years, he became NASA's Chief of the Astronaut Office, in charge of managing the astronauts.

Despite still being a part of the project, Shepard missed the potential to fly, as he underwent an operation in 1969 to correct his condition. The operation was successful, and he was reinstated into the program as an astronaut. His first assigned mission was the notorious *Apollo 13*, but he and his crew were pushed back to *Apollo 14* to give them more time to train. Following the problems with *Apollo 13*, NASA made changes to the craft, and Shepard and the crew of *Apollo 14* greatly benefited. During his first and only trip to the moon, Shepard got to play golf on the moon's surface. He and his crew member, Ed Mitchell, spent nine hours and seventeen minutes exploring and playing on the moon. After being away for thirty-three hours, Shepard and Mitchell returned to the craft, where Stuart Roosa had remained.

Shepard became one of a very small number of people to walk on the moon during the 20th century, and, at forty-seven years old, he had the distinction of being the oldest astronaut active with NASA. Shepard had two successful trips into space, logging nearly 217 hours in space. He returned to his role of managing the astronauts after his trip to the moon and finally retired in 1974. However, he continued to work, joining with other Mercury astronauts to start the Mercury Seven Foundation. This foundation was later called the Astronaut Scholarship Foundation, and today it helps fund college students studying a range of sciences and engineering. Shepard was later diagnosed with leukemia and died from complications of the illness in 1998.

The gap between when the Soviet Union achieved a milestone and when the US met that same milestone was closing. It took more than three months after *Sputnik 1* for the US to successfully launch *Explorer 1* into space. Less than three weeks after Gagarin became the first man in space, Shepard became the second.

Other Early Successful Trips

Just ten weeks after Shepard's launch into space, NASA prepared *Mercury 8*, which launched astronaut Virgil Ivan "Gus" Grissom into space on July 21, 1961. His time in space was comparable to Shepard's visit, lasting fifteen minutes. The craft had been adjusted, so Grissom was able to see Earth during his trip, and this wasn't the only change NASA made to the capsule: they changed the way the hatch would open after he splashed down in the ocean. There were several steps that had to be completed for the hatch to open, and it was this series of steps that would become a problem for Grissom.

Unlike Shepard's trip, when Grissom's capsule splashed down in the Atlantic Ocean, the capsule door opened prematurely. He had completed several of the steps, leaving the last one until the helicopter had appeared. Although he hadn't completed the full process, the door opened, and the capsule began to take on water and to sink. With no other choice, Grissom climbed out of the capsule in his spacesuit, which weighed more than twenty pounds. Astronauts spacesuits were designed to float, but this capability required certain steps to prepare—which Grissom did not have time to do before the capsule sank. As he treaded water, the suit began to fill up. It took five minutes before he was finally picked up, ending the struggle to survive. The recovery team did not realize that there was an issue because they had seen how buoyant the suites were. Believing him to be safe, they first moved to retrieve the capsule as it began to sink. As they struggled to pull out the water-filled craft, Grissom was left to try to remain afloat in his increasingly heavy suit.

Some of the recovery team said that Grissom worked to help with the craft recovery. Instead of swimming away from it, he put himself at further risk by remaining close to it. If the craft had sunk, it would have dragged Grissom down with it. Despite the situation, he directed the recovery efforts from his place near the capsule. When the craft was secured, he gave the recovery team two thumbs up to let them know they could start to pull it out of the water. At this point, the recovery team was almost entirely focused on retrieving the ship, so they failed to notice that Grissom himself was in danger. Grissom watched as they successfully lifted the capsule out of the water and water begin to spill out of it. A few waves quickly refilled the capsule, though, and they had to cut it loose.

A second helicopter came to retrieve Grissom only to notice that he was slipping under water. In a hurry to slip into the collar used to retrieve him, Grissom put it on backward but signaled for the crew to pull him up anyway.

The incident has spawned controversy, with some people saying that Grissom panicked and opened the door before he should have. This version was portrayed by Tom Wolfe, who described it as "screwing the pooch." Based on talks with people within NASA, however, Grissom was reacting to a calculated risk NASA had made. Rather than panicking, Grissom had been a quick-thinking hero who had almost single-handedly saved the space program with his actions.

The door opening was not his fault; he was simply reacting to a dire situation instead of freezing up and likely dying inside the capsule when it sank. The checklist that was established for opening the hatch was more of a guideline because the process had not been tested after a flight. Grissom was the first to go through it and had not been trained on the new mechanisms. Those who worked closely with him, as well as the senior NASA managers, believed he had acted appropriately for his situation.

Today, NASA would use this as a sign that things needed to be changed. In 1961, this was not an option because of the Space Race. Instead of being hailed a hero like Shepard, Grissom was the first American to have to justify and face scrutiny for his actions. After this, he would spend much of the rest of his career under a cloud.

Because of his fast thinking and quick reaction, Grissom could be credited with helping to keep the program going. About two months before his trip, President Kennedy had announced the intention to get a person on the moon. Had Grissom died, it would have given the president reason to reconsider and potentially slow the project. Grissom became dedicated to making sure things went right after that, and he spent a lot of time learning how the Gemini worked when NASA switched to the second program. He became the first person to make a second trip into space.

Grissom's tenacity and dedication earned him considerable respect within NASA, and he was chosen to be the captain of the three-member crew of *Apollo 1*. He and the other two crew members, Edward White and Roger Chaffee, died when the oxygen-rich capsule caught fire during a rehearsal. Some of the senior members of NASA have since admitted that had he lived, Grissom would have been their choice to be the first man on the moon since he had been in the program longer than anyone else.

Soon after Grissom's successful trip to space, Gherman Titov became the second Soviet to enter space, and he spent far longer in space than Gagarin. Both Soviets had managed to accomplish more than the short trips completed by the astronauts.

Titov was one of the finalists to be the first man in space, but there were good reasons why he was not ultimately chosen for the distinction. Unlike Gagarin, Titov had a temper that had gotten him into trouble on a few occasions (some even say it was one of the reasons he was not selected to be the first cosmonaut in space). It was said that he and Gagarin clashed, largely because of Titov's temper. Only slightly taller than Gagarin, at five-foot four inches, he was still small enough to fit into the capsule, yet his study build and athletic history made him ideal for the second trip, which would be considerably longer than a single trip around the Earth.

Titov himself would later indicate that he agreed with the choice to send Gagarin into space first, especially since the first man in space would spend a lot of time traveling around the Soviet Union talking to people. According to Titov, "It was Gagarin's character that mattered most. [Yuri] turned out to be the man that everyone loved. Me, they couldn't love ... I'm not lovable. I have a very explosive character. I could easily say rude things, offend someone, and walk away. I wasn't a very convenient person for the leadership; I had my own opinion about things and knew how to insist on things. This did not always stir up warm feelings ... but Yuri could talk freely to anyone— he could speak their language. The first man in space had to be a nice, attractive person ... they were right to choose [Yuri]."

Titov's flight was the second for the Soviet Union, but he was the fourth person into space (Shepard and Gus Grissom had both gone into space by the time he launched). He took off on August 6, 1961, becoming only the second person to orbit the Earth. He was the first person to spend more than a day in space, with his mission lasting twenty-five hours and eighteen minutes. He returned to Earth and became another Soviet hero.

He would later have another first that is far less known. A few months before his flight, Titov and his wife lost a baby son because of a heart defect. A few years after his trip into space, they would have a healthy daughter, making her the first child who was born to a person who had gone into space. He did not return to space, instead becoming a deputy of the Supreme Soviet. When the Soviet Union ended in 1991, he moved into politics, voted into the Russian parliament in 1995. He died in 2000.

John Glenn was one of the original seven astronauts in Project Mercury. On February 20, 1962, he became the fifth person in space and the first American to fully orbit the Earth. Three women working with computers back at NASA ensure his trip was a success: Mary Jackson, Dorothy Vaughan, and Katherine Johnson. Like Shepard, Glenn became an immediate American hero. His mission lasted four hours and fifty-five minutes. He would also utter one of the most famous quotes about what it was like to be one of the first people in space: "I felt exactly how you would feel if you were getting ready to launch and knew you were sitting on top of two million parts—all built by the lowest bidder on a government contract." It was perhaps as close as any of the astronauts came to criticizing NASA, but was certainly a fair critic of their situation. The men were already putting their lives on the line to see what was possible, while the government chose contracts that would help them keep the budget from continuing to balloon. This would prove to be something that would later come back to haunt NASA in the 1980s.

Glenn retired from space travel in 1964, but he would not stay away for long. In 1974, he was elected to the US Senate, serving as a senator for Ohio. He would be repeatedly elected to serve in the Senate, and he became one of the Senate's leading experts in science and technology. He retired from the Senate in 1997. The next year, he returned to space, making him the oldest person to go into space at that time. During the flight, he helped to study the aging process, spending longer in space during this last trip than his previous visit—a total of nine days. Glenn died in 2016, making him the last of the original astronauts to pass.

First Woman in Space

While NASA debated about adding women to the astronaut rosters (something the men in the program seem to have opposed: Glenn made a speech that largely said it wasn't the woman's role in American society), the USSR had far fewer problems with the concept of women participating in the Space Race.

Due to this difference, the Soviets quickly earned distinction for putting the first woman into space two decades before the US did. Inspired by Gagarin's trip into space, Valentina Tereshkova joined the cosmonaut program. While she had no experience as a pilot, she had been an active member of the Yaroslavl Air Sports Club and completed 126 successful parachute jumps. Since cosmonauts were ejected from their capsules, this made her an ideal candidate. She and four other women underwent eighteen months of training very similar to what the men went through.

Chosen to be the pilot of *Vostok 6*, Tereshkova was the only woman of the five to make the trip into space on June 16, 1963, two days after Valery Bykovsky was sent into space in *Vostok 5*. The pair conducted different orbits and passed close to each other, testing communications as they passed. Her image and time in the capsule were broadcast back to the USSR as she logged over seventy hours and nearly fifty rotations around the Earth.

During her time in space, there was a problem with the automatic navigation software, causing her craft to start moving away from the planet. When she noticed, she received a new set of algorithms from the scientists back on Earth. She returned safely, close to the Kazakhstan-Mongolian-Chinese border. Her face was bruised, but she was otherwise unharmed. Instead of going for the required medical tests, she went with the recovery team to get dinner first, something that earned her a reprimand.

Though few knew of the near disaster, Valentina was hailed as a hero. Like Gagarin, she would become a spokesperson for the

Soviets. Though she didn't return to space, she did become a test pilot and earned a doctorate. In 1963, she married another cosmonaut, Andriyan Nikolayev. They became the first couple in human history to have both gone into space and then have a child together. Their daughter received attention from the medical field because of this, and later, she herself became a doctor.

Tereshkova had continued to talk about her time in space and became a member of the effort for cooperation in space travel with other nations. She is still alive and an active member of the space community.

Chapter 9 – JFK's Resolve and Prediction of the Ultimate Win – Reaching the Moon

In the early 1960s, the Space Race was heating up as the two nations managed to send people into space. On September 12, 1962, President John F. Kennedy delivered a speech to stir the American people's emotions and enthusiasm for the efforts to travel in space. Known today as the "Moon Speech," this oratory helped bring more focus to the American effort in space exploration, which had lost some luster since the Soviets continually beat the US to major milestones.

Speaking in front of a crowd at Rice University in Houston, Texas, the president focused not on what had happened (Shepard, Grissom, and Glenn had all successfully gone into space, but the Soviets had done more with their two, who both orbited the Earth), but on what he wanted to happen. He had first talked about going to the moon the year before, but the USSR had repeatedly done more since that time. By refocusing the country's efforts on what was possible, he inspired more people to support the program. Kennedy didn't just state the plan to put a man on the moon—he made it an American objective that received the funding it needed to ensure it was achieved before the close of the decade.

The speech was a part of a larger tour that included a visit to Houston, Florida, and Alabama (three key locations for NASA's work). With people beginning to question why the US was involved in the race, Kennedy emphasized that it wasn't just about beating the Soviets, but about pushing boundaries as a part of the American dream. To a crowd of about 40,000 people, he spoke some of the words he is best known for uttering during his presidency:

> For the eyes of the world now look into space, to the moon and to the planets beyond, and we have vowed that we shall not see it governed by a hostile flag of conquest, but by a banner of freedom and peace. We have vowed that we shall not see space filled with weapons of mass destruction, but with instruments of knowledge and understanding.
>
> Yet the vows of this nation can only be fulfilled if we in this nation are first, and, therefore, we intend to be first. In short, our leadership in science and in industry, our hopes for peace and security, our obligations to ourselves as well as others, all require us to make this effort, to solve these mysteries, to solve them for the good of all men, and to become the world's leading space-faring nation.
>
> We choose to go to the moon. We choose to go to the moon in this decade and do the other things, not because they are easy, but because they are hard, because that goal will serve to organize and measure the best of our energies and skills, because that challenge is one that we are willing to accept, one we are unwilling to postpone, and one which we intend to win, and the others, too.

> \-   *President John F. Kennedy*

His argument was that space travel was inevitable. If the US did not continue to push forward, the Soviets would gain the upper hand, making space far more hostile (the Soviets had a similar concern if the US gained the upper hand). By abdicating that lead, the US was failing in its responsibilities to use its technology and abilities to their fullest extent.

One reason Kennedy did not focus on the past but rather set this ambitious goal was that it was an area in which the Soviets did not already have a substantial head start. With Gagarin becoming the first person in space, the US needed a longer-range goal that would give the country a good chance of succeeding first. Kennedy and his administration consulted with their best scientist, von Braun, to see what was realistic. Von Braun said that the best sporting chance the US had was with the goal of reaching the moon. The US had bigger capsules, which gave it a lead over the USSR.

The speech set an incredibly difficult goal, but it had originally included a shorter timeframe: he was supposed to announce the goal of landing on the moon by 1967. This would have been a way of noting the 50th anniversary of the Bolshevik Revolution and could have helped to push the Soviets to agree to engage in the challenge that the president had issued. Fortunately, Kennedy realized before he started his speech that the timelines was perhaps too ambitious and changed the wording so that it simply said by the end of the decade.

Kennedy was assassinated a few years later, but his vision was realized as Americans would be the first on the moon (the Soviets never succeeded in orbiting the moon, let alone landing on it), and they would reach this major milestone in 1969 before the decade ended.

His words still resonate today, though for different reasons. NASA's funding would start to be reduced after the US had shown its dominance in space, but any efforts to close parts of the agency have been easily denied. This is largely because space still inspires people to do more. Some even credit the speech with pushing the US to meet the goal expressed by a president who was killed in office. Money poured into Project Apollo, and it is estimated that the full project cost $25 billion (an estimated $100 billion today with inflation). Though some experts believe people would have inevitably walked on the moon, even they think it could have taken decades. Given how quickly funding into NASA cooled after Apollo's success, it's also possible the milestone may not have been met as quickly without Kennedy's rousing speech.

What is certain is that without the speech and the Space Race, the push to get to the moon would have been much weaker and would have likely remained only within a small community. As it was, Kennedy made it a point of national pride and interest that gave Americans a common goal and a set timeline by which to accomplish it.

Chapter 10 – The Three Primary NASA Programs

Because of the secretive nature of the Soviet's space program, it is far more difficult to dive into the details of their work. They did keep documents of their progress, but many of them were only released at the end of the 20th century and early 21st century. NASA was far more open about their work because the US wanted to make space exploration an international effort. They did keep some elements secret, particularly the technology used to achieve some of their most impressive feats, but they published a considerable amount of information about their primary projects. Unlike the USSR, space exploration in the US was established to be something for everyone, not just the military. There was a crossover between the technology and knowledge applied to space travel and used in the military (and astronauts were often selected from military pilots), but much of what the US learned was shared with the world.

The three primary projects that NASA established are well-documented within the media and archives, giving people a way to look back at how they were received and what kinds of expectations were established for each of them.

Project Mercury – 1961 until 1963

One thing no one knew at the beginning of 1961 was if it was even possible to send someone into space. It was known that Laika had survived for a while in space (most of the world was still under the impression she had survived for most of the orbits), but that didn't necessarily mean it would be possible for a person to withstand the same experience based on what a person requires compared to a dog, particularly in terms of oxygen. Since the USSR provided not real information with their announcement, the US had no idea just what to expect from the launch of a larger animal into space, let alone what would happen to a person. This would serve as the first obvious goal for the US, followed by information on how they could sustain life for longer periods of time. They would take a very measured approach to accomplish this, setting the stage for how the other two projects would be set up.

The primary objective of Project Mercury was to assess if humans could withstand the experience, what was needed to sustain human life in space, and to begin understanding what could be accomplished. At this point, they weren't sure that a trip to the moon was possible. The early Mercury missions focused on sending a single person into space using vessels that were specifically designed for the project. However, there was room to cut the project short in the event that they were able to accomplish the primary objective early. Project Mercury was as much about establishing a realistic pace for what was possible and safe as it was about beating the Soviets. After all, there had been enough of an uproar among other nations following Laika's death that the US did not want to potentially face backlash from not completing its due diligence. They would also learn through this project just how expensive it was to train and prepare people for the trip into space.

Project Mercury had six missions, with the astronauts spending a total of thirty-four hours over the Earth. Shepard's mission was part of the Mercury project. Inspired by the success of the launch, Kennedy announced the intent of getting a man on the moon before the end of the decade. With more funds appropriated to the effort, NASA started planning to meet the goal of landing people on the moon. This did not mean that Project Mercury ended. NASA continued to send astronauts into space for brief periods to learn more about what people would need while orbiting in space.

Project Gemini – 1965 until 1966

Project Gemini built on the successful launches from Project Mercury. The first two launches (April 8, 1964 and January 19, 1965) were test missions and did not have crews. The first mission with a crew launched March 23, 1965, and returned to Earth the same day.

NASA used Gemini to learn more about what was possible in space. They tested how to maneuver in space, change orbit, dock with a rocket (they would need to dock with the main vehicle after reaching the moon's surface), and spend some time in space. All these activities were necessary for achieving the long-term goal of walking on the moon. The last mission, Gemini 12, included Jim Lovell and Buzz Aldrin and lasted from November 11, 1966, to November 15, 1966. Returning both men safely, NASA proved it could support life in space for more than just a short trip.

The longest mission had been that of *Gemini 7*, with a launch on December 4, 1965 and splashdown on December 18, 1965. The crew, Frank Borman and Jim Lovell, had spent two weeks in space. It was not known how long it would take to get a manned craft to the moon, so this trip showed NASA that it had the ability to sustain people for longer trips into space.

During all the missions, the crews had worked and done regular daily tasks. The cumulative results of each mission assured NASA it had its bases covered to plan a trip to the moon. Its scientists would be able to provide an environment in which astronauts could live and work for the duration of the trip to the moon, and the team had learned how to maneuver crafts in space, dock, and walk in space.

Project Apollo – 1967 until 1972

Easily the most famous of NASA's projects, Apollo was the one that finally saw the ultimate milestone – people walking on the moon and coming home safely. The project began with tragedy when the crew of *Apollo 1* was killed by fire in the oxygen-rich environment. Because of this tragedy, modifications were made to the cabin and craft.

Unmanned crafts were also tested. The first crew to enter space as a part of Project Apollo reached the moon's orbit, behind when the Soviets had reached the celestial object with their satellites. This was when the US really started to pull ahead in the Space Race, a position they retained over the rest of the competition. *Apollo 8* launched on December 21, 1968, and marked the first time the US had clearly taken the lead in the Space Race. The Soviet Union had reached the moon with *Luna 2*, but with several competing teams within the space program following Korolev's death, the focus was more on outperforming each other than beating the US. While the USSR contended with infighting, NASA continued to push the Apollo project, which completed two more successful missions to orbit the moon. During these missions, the lunar module was tested to see if astronauts could dock and undock to the main craft. *Apollo 11* would be the mission and spacecraft that made history with the first two people to walk on the moon.

Following the success of *Apollo 11*, NASA completed six more missions with varying degrees of success. Each mission purposed to have its teams visit and study different parts of the moon. After *Apollo 11*, the *Apollo 13* mission is probably the next most famous, as an explosion prevented the crew from reaching the moon. While the primary objective was a failure, NASA proved its ability to overcome the unexpected and resolve crises. The team still went around the moon and returned home safely, inspiring the movie, *Apollo 13*, several decades later.

The last mission was *Apollo 17*, launching on December 11, 1972, and returning December 19, 1972. Six Apollo missions successfully landed on the moon, and significant data was collected during these trips. The crews returned with rocks, dirt, and other things from the moon's surface, totaling about 880 pounds of samples.

Chapter 11 – The First Spacewalks

With both the USSR and US working to be the first on the moon, there were many other firsts. One milestone would be critical for any real time in space: the ability to safely spacewalk. If anything happened to the spacecraft, people would need to be able to safely exit and make repairs. It was also necessary to know how people would react to space since they would be exposed to it on the moon's surface. Both sides needed to determine how to design spacesuits that would allow people to survive outside the controlled environment of their space capsules.

The Soviets were the first to successfully complete a spacewalk. On March 18, 1965, cosmonaut Alexei Leonov exited his *Voskhod 2* and spent twelve minutes outside the craft. There were many things no one could have known about being outside of the protection of a spacecraft, and Leonov would be uncomfortable. Some who analyzed the data from his experience described it as miserable. As he floated in open space, his temperature rose sharply, putting him at risk of heatstroke. Outside the protection of *Voskhod 2*, he was exposed to the vacuum of space, which caused issues no one had anticipated. His spacesuit expanded, so when he headed back to the hatch to reenter the vessel, he had to exert himself—something that was difficult since he was already close to overheating. Having reentered *Voskhod 2*, Leonov returned safely to Earth. He would later relate that the sound he most remembered was the sound of his own breathing, which he described as labored.

Since the Soviets did not share much of what they learned, the US would largely learn about the dangers of space on its own. However, it had also collected much more data to better plan for the possible conditions. Therefore, its spacesuits would not have the kinds of problems Leonov experienced. A few months after the Soviet spacewalk, NASA sent Edward White into space to conduct the first American spacewalk on June 3, 1965. This was part of the *Gemini IV* mission, and it proved to be a very different experience for the American. Remaining in space for nearly twice as long, at twenty-three minutes, White reportedly said, "I feel like a million dollars." His tasks were also far different: instead of remaining still in space, he had a hand-held zip gun, which he used to move around. Like many other US missions, this was televised, so the recording of White using the little zip gun to enjoy his experience can still be watched today. When the gun ran out of fuel, he was basically done. As he returned, one of the extra gloves floated out of the open hatch. Knowing he had to return to the ship, White was reported to have called the end of his time in space "... the saddest moment of my life."

The next spacewalk happened on June 5, 1966, when Eugene Cernan was given a chance to leave the vessel during the *Gemini 9* mission. Given White's reaction, most people thought Cernan would have as much fun, particularly as he was given a backpack to help him maneuver. The backpack was located outside of the craft, though, meaning that Cernan had to go retrieve it. Without any means of controlling his motions to reach it, the astronaut had to move towards it using the few handholds on the ship. Consequently, he was spun around. The uncontrollable motions, coupled with the risky task, caused his heart rate to increase to 155 beats per minute. His visor became so foggy he could no longer see. Though his spacesuit size was not a problem, his near blindness made it even harder for him to reenter the craft than what Leonov had experienced. Cernan did not enjoy the experience, comparing it to trying to put a cork back into a champagne bottle.

Buzz Aldrin would be the last American to walk in space before the US reached the moon. His trip was on November 13, 1966, rounding out the spacewalks for Project Gemini. During this mission, Aldrin would leave the craft several times. His was the longest spacewalk, lasting two hours as he moved around the outside of the craft on a tether, taking pictures and looking at the world. He added to a map of the stars and collected some micrometeorite samples. In total, Aldrin spent nearly five and a half hours in space between the three trips in and out of the craft.

The Soviet's next successful spacewalk was in January of 1969 and involved two cosmonauts spacewalking at the same time. Boris Volynov was the commander who stayed on the *Soyuz 5*. Aleksei Yeliseyev and Yevgeny Khrunov left the vessel to board *Soyuz 4*, which was commanded by Vladimir Shatalov. The two men successfully transferred to the other vessel, though there was a problem when Volynov reentered Earth. He survived but lost some teeth when he was tossed across *Soyuz 5*'s cockpit.

Chapter 12 – The First Successful Spacecraft Docking

One of the last major hurdles to reaching the moon was the ability to dock in space since no vehicle could be sent directly to the moon. As this was impossible to replicate on Earth, it became one of the last major missions of Project Gemini. On March 16, 1966, *Gemini 8* launched from Cape Canaveral, Florida. Aboard the craft were Neil Armstrong and David Scott, who would be in space for three days to complete several tasks. The primary objective was for the two men to complete a series of four docking tests. This was a necessary step in finally reaching the moon as NASA was working on the Lunar Module. The craft that the astronauts would be in as they went to the moon was not meant to land on its surface. Instead, the Lunar Module would be used by the two people who would walk on the moon. After leaving the moon, the astronauts would need to dock with the main craft before starting the return trip to Earth.

There had been two earlier Gemini missions (6 and 7) in which the crew had successfully rendezvoused in space but had not attempted to dock. This was one milestone the US achieved first in a series of first that increasingly went to the capitalist nation, particularly after the main Soviet scientist, Korolev, died in 1966. Without him, the Soviets would fall behind as members of their space teams vied for control and competed against each other. Korolev had largely been their unifying leader, which became clear after his passing.

During the Gemini mission, Scott was scheduled to complete several extra-vehicular activities (EVA), which would build on White's spacewalk the previous year. Armstrong was in command, and after they had completed five orbits in six hours, he moved the craft toward Agena-D to begin docking. Scott would later describe the experience, saying they fell silent as they listened for signs that the docking was going as planned. Armstrong and Scott heard their first contact with the target vessel, followed by the unmistakable sound of the latches locking into place. They said it was surprisingly easy.

This early success was quickly disrupted by issues. Before they could celebrate, Scott noticed that the 8-ball the commander had given with them was rolling, which it shouldn't have done in space. To conserve the fuel on the Gemini craft, the crew had used the Agena's engine to complete the docking. They turned this off, which momentarily stopped the toy's movement. But then it began to roll faster. The pair were rotating along all three axes (yaw, pitch, and roll). Mission Control had advised them to undock if they had problems, which Armstrong did. Once they were separated, the crew began trying to steady the Gemini. This was when they realized the problem was with *Gemini 8*, not Agena. They would later learn that one of the maneuver systems on the *Gemini 8* had short-circuited and was perpetually firing.

Calling ground control, they reported they were having an issue as Gemini tumbled end over end through space. It's estimated that they were completing a revolution every second, and it was beginning to make both men very dizzy. Thinking quickly, Armstrong disabled the OAMS thrusters and activated the thrusters at the front of the craft, which helped it to stabilize.

Though they had planned to do a lot more, both men knew that protocol called for them to head home. They did not know what was causing the problem, so they needed to return to have the spacecraft assessed. Despite the problem, they had successfully docked. This mission was a partial success, but having failed to complete all of the initially planned tasks, it was not considered a complete success. They have managed to prove that it was possible—even easy—to dock with another craft without an astronaut having to go outside. This was at least a reliable proof of concept, so NASA was able to move forward with the Gemini Project. Despite the mixed success of the mission, it did end up in the *Guinness World Records* as the first time two craft docked in space. The record does address the fact that the spacewalks were scrapped because the thrusts malfunctioned.

Gemini 10 would successfully complete the rest of the original *Gemini 8* tasks with the crew members John Young and Michael Collins.

In 1967, the Soviets completed the first unmanned docking in space. Then, in January 1969, they would successfully dock with crew members. Since the USSR was the only other country to be working in space at the time, they did get a mention in the *Guinness World Records*, as well. It further mentions that the crew members were able to successfully switch.

Chapter 13 – Apollo 11 – One Small Step for Man

Though the Apollo project started in tragedy, it ultimately gave the US an undeniable lead in the Space Race. The USSR would never catch up to the American accomplishments.

On July 20, 1969, NASA successfully sent a crew to the moon, and two of the three men successfully landed on the surface before later returning.

Planning

Following the disaster and tragedy of *Apollo 1*, NASA waited almost two years for the next manned mission to the moon to ensure that a similar disaster did not happen again. They had lost three men on Earth, and this reminded everyone just how dangerous space exploration was, even before astronauts reached space.

Three men were chosen to crew *Apollo 11*: Commander Neil Armstrong, Buzz Aldrin, and Michael Collins. All the men had a unique history that made them ideal for their respective roles. At thirty-eight-years-old, Armstrong had commanded two missions and was the first civilian to do so. Aldrin, a year older, was the first astronaut to have a doctorate. His intellect made him an ideal choice as the pilot of the Lunar Module. Finally, Collins had successfully walked in space during *Gemini 10*.

Collins was assigned the role of remaining on the Apollo spacecraft while Armstrong and Aldrin would board the Lunar Module and walk on the moon's surface. Prior to the mission, the men had not worked together, but once they were selected, they went through a rigorous training program that lasted six months. All three of them had been in successful missions, but this was their first time working on a mission together.

The Launch and Landing on the Moon

On July 16, 1969, the three-member crew lifted off from Cape Canaveral, Florida, at 9:32 a.m. Cameras were rolling to capture the launch, and the crew filmed themselves twice during their flight. Their third transmission gained far more attention than the other broadcasts because the surface of the moon could be seen from the craft. It took four days, but on July 20, 1969, Armstrong and Aldrin went aboard the Lunar Module, called the "Eagle," and set off for the moon's surface.

Aldrin landed the Eagle in what is called the Sea of Tranquility, a sizeable basaltic region of the moon. Upon their successfully landing, Armstrong reported back to mission control: "Houston, Tranquility Base here. The Eagle has landed." After this, the two men did not rush out the door, as many people today imagine. Instead, they spent two hours doing a comprehensive systems' check, setting them so that the Lunar Module would remain on the moon. They were about to exit a craft without any tether, so they wanted to make sure it didn't drift away or have any problems that would strand them on the moon's surface. They also had a meal.

One Giant Leap for Mankind

After those two hours, the cameras were turned on, and people watched as Armstrong exited the Eagle. At 11:56 p.m., Armstrong made history as he took the first step on the moon and uttered one of the most well-known quotes in human history: "That's one small step for man, one giant leap for mankind." About twenty minutes later, Aldrin's exit from the Eagle was captured by Armstrong from the moon's surface. Images of the time are mostly of Aldrin since, as the commander, Armstrong was responsible for documenting the entire mission and was the one taking the pictures. Given the difficulty of telling the difference between them in their large spacesuits, this is something that often goes unnoticed by people today.

It was not enough for the men to simply land on the moon and return, though. NASA was dedicated to getting as much scientific data as possible from each mission and, considering this was the first time anyone had landed on the moon, there were many tasks Armstrong and Aldrin were expected to complete before returning home. They completed several experiments and collected samples from the moon's surface. One of the most interesting tasks they completed while still on the moon was calling President Richard Nixon.

A somber element was added to the trip as they placed medals on the planet to commemorate astronauts and cosmonauts who had died, including Gagarin and the three crew members of *Apollo 1*. While the Space Race may have caused tensions between the two countries, the people who had been to space felt a sense of comradery that made nationality irrelevant. The competition did not negate what the other nation had accomplished, and those who died in the pursuit of space exploration deserved to be remembered.

Since NASA had worked with scientists from many other nations, a disk that included messages provided by seventy-three countries was left on the moon. The astronauts also left a plaque with the following words:

> Here men from the planet earth
>
> First set foot upon the moon
>
> July 1969, A.D.
>
> We came in peace for all mankind

Though there was certainly a sense of international backing, Armstrong and Aldrin planted the US flag on the moon, providing a visible symbol of who had reached the moon first.

During their time on the moon, the two had moved up to 200 feet away from the Eagle when they headed into a crater on the moon's surface. When they left, they took more than forty-five pounds of samples with them. They reported that moving around on the moon's surface was far easier than they had imagined. Armstrong had been out of the craft for about two and a half hours when he reentered the Eagle.

When the Eagle left the moon, it had spent twenty-one and a half hours on the surface, or nearly a full day. At 1:54 p.m., they returned to the *Columbia* with the samples they had collected. This time, Armstrong got to experience a much smoother docking experience. Back on the craft, they began their return to Earth.

On July 24, 1969, at 12:50 p.m., Armstrong and Aldrin splashed down in the Pacific Ocean. They were recovered, then immediately put into isolation suits since it wasn't certain if anything harmful could have returned with them from the moon. Once they had been scrubbed with iodine, they boarded a helicopter to start their trek back to Houston. When they reached Houston, they began quarantine, which lasted until August 10, 1969.

Armstrong largely moved into a more private life. He died on August 25, 2012. Aldrin and Collins continued to speak as members of the Apollo project well into their 80s, and both men were still alive as of 2020.

A Unique Accomplishment

The Soviet Union failed to land on the moon, and more than fifty years later, no other nation besides the US has successfully landed on the moon. The last time the US went to the moon was in 1972. Attempting to travel to the moon now would mean returning to the drawing board because there have been many advances, particularly in terms of digital technology. While some nations are working to land on the moon, there is neither a strong incentive to spur them to action, like the speech delivered by President Kennedy, nor a fierce competition like that between the US and USSR from the 1950s to the 1970s.

The Space Race continued, but it slowed significantly after the final Apollo trip to the moon. Both nations focused on other areas of space travel. The US moved toward developing space shuttles, which would provide a more easily-controlled way of landing after reentering Earth's atmosphere. These craft would not be able to land on the moon. The USSR largely focused on working on satellites, as it was less costly to send unmanned vehicles into space.

Even if it wasn't the end of the Space Race, there were no more inspiring milestones that could compare to the ones up to this point (going to Mars was far beyond the capability of either nation). While there would still be plenty of other firsts both nations achieved, there hasn't been the same amount of interest or dedication of funds since 1972. The modern-day public seems to take it for granted that people can walk on the moon, but it will take a considerable rethinking of how to do it and nearly as many years to accomplish as the amount of time between Kennedy's 1962 speech and the first step Armstrong took in 1969.

Chapter 14 – Those Who Gave Their Lives

All the people who elected to be cosmonauts and astronauts entered their respective programs knowing the risks. What they were doing was comparable to what Europeans had done when they headed to the New World across an ocean. However, unlike those travelers, the people who chose to go into space did so knowing there would be no help if something happened. No ship could come by to save them. Space was an unknown frontier where anything that went wrong would spell death for those aboard their vessels. *Apollo 13* is perhaps the most well-known example of how things could have gone wrong (largely because of the movie it inspired several decades later).

Unfortunately, there were times when people were not successful in escaping death. Given how little was known about space and what conditions were the most stable for human life, there were times when practicing for potential issues and conditions led to the death of astronauts and cosmonauts while still on Earth.

Cosmonauts Who Are Known to Have Perished During Their Duties

Only since the Space Race ended has the USSR (and later Russia) begun to release details about its space program and the number of cosmonauts who died become public knowledge.

While preparing to launch the first person into space, the USSR began training cosmonauts in an oxygen-rich environment. The cosmonaut in the training cabin at the time died in a fire that quickly got out of control. Had the Soviets shared what they learned during this tragedy, other lives could have been saved.

For a long time, the first known cosmonaut to die was Vladimir Komarov. When the *Soyuz 1* parachute was deployed, it failed to open. He plummeted to Earth, dying on April 24, 1967.

While undocking from the Salyut 1 space station, the crew of the *Soyuz 11* headed home on June 30, 1971. Roughly thirty minutes before returning to Earth, one of the key valves presumably opened, causing the cabin to decompress. The three cosmonauts, Georgi Dobrovolski, Vladislav Volkov, and Viktor Patsayev, would have died instantly. When the craft landed, people opened the door and found the three cosmonauts deceased. Until the early 21ˢ century, they were the only three people to die in space.

It is unknown how many cosmonauts perished since the accuracy of the Soviet records is questionable. It is possible that the number of people who are known to have died completing their duties is accurate, but it is also possible that the records were misrepresented, like what was broadcasted about Laika. It took decades before her actual fate became known. Still, the information was eventually released, suggesting there may not be additional deaths.

Astronauts Who Perished

Technically, there are no US astronauts who died in space. That does not mean the nation has a spotless record. More than a few astronauts have perished while training or during different phases of missions.

The first astronaut to die was Theodore Freeman while testing a T-38 on October 31, 1964. During the test, it struck a goose. Parts of the vehicle broke apart and were sucked into the engines. Though he successfully ejected from the vehicle, Freeman was too close to the ground for his parachute to fully deploy, and he died.

Two astronauts, Charles Bassett and Elliot See, the chosen crew members for *Gemini 9*, were killed while aboard a T-38. Another astronaut, Clifton Williams, would also die while aboard a T-38.

As related previously, the original crew of *Apollo 1*, Virgil Grissom, Roger Chaffee, and Edward White, died while training for the mission in Cape Kennedy. NASA had constructed a training exercise in an oxygen-rich environment. As the Soviets had learned a few years earlier, this was a risky environment. When a fire started in the cabin, the astronauts perished before anyone could get to them.

Michael Adams was not officially an astronaut when he went aboard the X-15 on November 15, 1967. The vehicle broke up while he was in flight, killing him. He would be given the title of astronaut posthumously.

Perhaps the most well-known fatal American incident occurred on January 28, 1986. With the Space Race cooling and few new milestones achieved the previous few years, launches had not attracted much attention. But, for the first time, NASA was sending up a civilian. After a long competition, a teacher, Sharon (Christa) McAuliffe, was selected to join six astronauts on the space shuttle *Challenger*. The day of the launch was cold, causing the failure of an O-ring that was a part of the rocket motors. When the motor began to leak exhaust, other parts of the structure began to fail. The shuttle had launched on time, but seventy-three seconds later, as it was going up into the sky, the shuttle exploded. All seven people aboard died:

- Commander Dick Scobee

- Pilot Michael Smith

- Gregory Jarvis (Payload Specialist)

- Judy Resnik (Mission Specialist)

- Ronald McNair (Mission Specialist)

- Ellison Onizuka (Mission Specialist)

- Sharon (Christa) McAuliffe (teacher and first citizen to be selected for space travel)

The Space Race ended in 1991, but others who have died in the pursuit of furthering science in the US. All members aboard the space shuttle *Columbia* perished when the space shuttle disintegrated while returning to Earth. Up to that point, the mission had been successful.

Others Who Died in the Name of Space Exploration

The previous section covered the people who volunteered to go into space knowing the risks, but many other people died while testing equipment and during launches. Like many other scientific fields, space flight holds a significant element of risk for those involved. For example, estimates say between 78 and 160 people were killed when one of the 1960 Soviet launches went very wrong, killing nearly every present, including some higher Soviet officials.

Still, it is a field that inspires and stimulates the imagination. Despite the dangers, it still attracts attention, and people are eager to contribute to space exploration. With as much as the US and USSR accomplished during the Space Race, there are still so many first left to be achieved. Knowing the risks, people are still interested in seeing what they can contribute.

The loss of the brave people who were willing to risk their lives in the name of exploration and scientific advancement is tragic. Nevertheless, both the Soviet and American programs had impressive safety records considering the dangers of space travel, particularly in the early days. As more nations and businesses become interested in seeing what they can achieve, the number of deaths has continued to rise. Just as with aviation, there are simply risks that come with space training and travel. Space travel is still far from being safe enough for commercial flights, but over time, it will hopefully become as reliable as flight.

Chapter 15 – The Long, Bumpy Road to Coordination

Fear of losing technical and military superiority had led both nations to push themselves and their scientists to be superior to the other's. The Space Race helped create two of the most advanced and outstanding programs the world has seen. By the 1980s, the drive for superiority had mostly disappeared. Both nations had spent substantial amounts on their programs. The USSR's program was starting to have problems and stumble, making it difficult to dedicate funds to a project that had not seen any successes as inspirational as those achieved under Korolev.

The US had been pushing for a greater contingent of nations working together for the peaceful advancement of space exploration with the help of the United Nations (UN), which responded by creating a committee dedicated to the cause. Eventually, the USSR would join, though not in the early years. The Committee on Space Research was a similar effort headed by the international scientific community. This committee mandated that both the US and USSR appoint their vice presidents to the committee, with the purpose of starting a dialogue between the two biggest participants in the Space Race. Academician Anatoli Blagonravov was the representative for the

USSR. There was a complication with this appointment, though, since the Soviet military insisted on providing its approval before anything was finalized. By comparison, the US had long been working with other nations, with NASA providing a single umbrella for these efforts. As a civilian agency (not a military one), remained focused on science instead of military developments. This meant that NASA could more easily obtain resources, jointly develop ideas within the scientific community, and rethink technology. The Soviet advances made in the early days of the Space Race were unsustainable, and the isolation that the USSR experienced as time pressed on led it to fall behind after the death of Korolev in 1966.

The US and USSR had periodically tried to collaborate since 1960. The Space Race had proved to be a very expensive endeavor, making a collaborative effort desirable for financial reasons. It would also allow them to know what kind of technology each had, which could have alleviated some of the tensions of the Cold War. Eisenhower's initiative, called "Atoms for Peace," nearly brought the two superpowers together as they planned a summit for April of 1960. Unfortunately, the summit was canceled when a US spy plane was shot down over USSR territories.

US President John F. Kennedy would continue to try for a more cooperative approach with the USSR. The day he assumed office, his inaugural address clearly stated this desire. In 1961, he called for this effort to begin: "Let both sides seek to invoke the wonders of science instead of its terrors. Together let us explore the stars." Khrushchev was unmoved by this call, especially as the USSR seemed to be superior in its approach and were already planning to send the first man into space. The Soviet media displayed their superior abilities, giving them no incentive to accept the US's call to work together. The problem with this approach would later be more obvious. The USSR was so focused on accomplishing a range of firsts that it failed to conduct the same levels of scientific research the US had completed with its earliest satellites. The US was not that far behind the Soviet

Union in its firsts, while the gap between the nations' understanding of space and meteorological data was significant: the US had a lot more knowledge than the USSR.

Following the successful trip made by John Glenn in February 1962, Khrushchev finally reached out to discuss a more collaborative effort. The two sides began to talk, leading to an agreement that they would work together in three keep areas:

> 1. The two sides would exchange weather data and have a coordinated launch effort for any meteorological satellites.

> 2. They would work together to map Earth's geomagnetic field.

> 3. They would make an effort toward experimental communications.

This work would benefit both nations since they were the only two countries capable of exploring space to any significant extent. Coordinated efforts to track the weather would provide them with safer launches and retrievals, and being able to communicate would potentially help avoid problems. The effort was not treated equally. The USSR classified everything as secret and rarely disclosed information to the US; the US tended to share their information. Even if it had not shared data with the USSR, the US tended to share data and knowledge with other nations, making the information easier for spies to find.

Following Khrushchev being pushed out of office in 1964, the next premier, Leonid Brezhnev, took a much stronger stance against the collaboration. Aware that the US was in a better position in terms of missile capabilities, he strove to create a force that would better rival what the Americans had achieved.

The next four years would see the USSR continue to fall behind the US, and they watched as Americans walked on the moon while they were far from capable of any similar achievement. Seeing that their dominance and superiority was over, the Soviets had more reasons to work with the US, though they had less leverage now that it was clear the US had progressed beyond their capabilities. Still, they were not willing to admit the current state of their program and changed their focus to establishing a robotic presence in space, which was much cheaper than sending people into space. The two space programs finally began to diverge as the US focused on developing better methods of traveling into space while the Soviets looked for better ways of remaining in space. Ultimately, this led to the US developing space shuttles while the USSR would eventually create a space station.

A movie called *Marooned* would ultimately help bring the two nations together. The plot of the movie had two Americans trapped in Earth's orbit being saved by Soviet cosmonauts. This fictitious image of how important a collaborative effort between the two was essential for success resonated within the small space community, and scientists on both sides saw the value of working together. After all, not many people on the planet had the knowledge necessary to help, and with few people in space, helping each other made more sense than perishing out of pride. A new push for working together came in 1975 via the Apollo-Soyuz Test Project, a docking mission that would successfully occur in July. After the successful docking, a bilateral working group was established to further develop a more collaborative effort between the two nations. However, this would not last long. President Jimmy Carter ended the cooperation, believing the USSR had obtained technology during the 1975 project. The two sides had begun to work more closely in other scientific fields, particularly life sciences and biomedical, but it would be several more years before they would make a more serious effort to combine their efforts in space.

The US had begun a program to examine other planets, largely staying out of space between 1975 and 1981. During this time, it was developing a space shuttle that would give astronauts better control over their flight during the landing process. The Soviets may not have traveled as much during this time, but they had sent cosmonauts to spend extended periods of time in space and learn about its effects on the body. This was knowledge the US did not have, as their longest missions up to that point were brief. As each nation had its own specialties, there was more communication between the two during the 1980s. Their relationship was still tense, but the Space Race tension had largely cooled. Having developed a friendlier relationship, the US and USSR worked together to study Halley's comet, a celestial object that comes close enough to be seen with the naked eye once every seventy-five years. Since the Soviets had more experience in space in recent years, they would use their own craft to study it from space while the US provided support from Earth. The US collected data about the comet as it drew close while the USSR and other nations in the Interagency Consultative Group participated in their mission (Vega 1 and 2 and the Giotto mission, respectively). The coordinated effort was very successful.

In 1984, President Ronald Reagan announced that NASA would begin developing a space station that would rival what the Soviet Union had accomplished, and he asked other nations to join. The USSR was excluded from this invitation, but there were talks with them behind the scenes. The US would more openly call for collaboration in October of that year. With the emergence of Mikhail Gorbachev as the new leader of the USSR, it appeared that this might finally be achieved in a more meaningful, long-term way.

Initially, the Soviets remained resistant to the idea that space and the military should be separated (the space program was always a part of the USSR military efforts). Following the explosion of the US space shuttle *Challenger* in January 1986, the USSR would find success when they launched part of what would later become the Mir space station less than a month later. With this achievement, they finally agreed to split their space efforts from their military work, though it is not known exactly what drove this decision. The two nations then established a five-year agreement by which they would coordinate several different projects (though none related to humans in space). In 1988, Regan was invited to join Gorbachev at the Kremlin. During Reagan's stay in the Soviet Union, Gorbachev tried to get him to agree to a joint effort to finally put a person on Mars. More than three decades later, this effort has yet to come to pass.

Conclusion

Though it wasn't intentionally started, the Space Race quickly became a heavy focus of both the US and USSR, the two superpowers that emerged after World War II. As nations began the long recovery process from the most destructive war in human history, the Allies quickly learned just how much more advanced the Nazis had been in terms of their weaponry and technology. The mistrust between most Allied nations and the USSR caused the rapid deterioration of cooperation, then more contentious and hostile interactions between the US and USSR became. This led to them each absorbing German scientists, most of whom had been a part of the Nazi Party, into their scientific communities. These Germans had been a part of many projects, including the development of an early ballistic missile. Though the USSR had a highly talented and knowledgeable scientist who was working space travel, the addition of the German scientists helped to speed up his work. The US would greatly benefit from their German scientists, as well.

As tensions between the US and USSR grew, they began to look for ways to show their superiority. Since the US had managed to be the first to develop nuclear weapons, it felt confident it was more advanced than its communist adversary. This led to complacency toward its current technology, especially as the cost of simply getting a satellite into space ballooned. This lasted until the surprising successful launch of *Sputnik 1*. As it passed over the US several times a day, it became clear that the US was already far behind the USSR, which had launched Sputnik in 1957. After that success, both nations increased their efforts to achieve a host of firsts, including getting the first person into space and back.

After several years of accomplishing a steady string of successes, the USSR would begin to falter in the Space Race, particularly after the death of Sergei Korolev in early 1966. Though the Soviet Union would achieve another major milestone by landing *Luna 9* on the moon, it was based on Korolev's work and was its last major success.

For nearly a decade, the Soviet Union had been the leader in most aspects of the Space Race. On July 16, 1969, the US launched *Apollo 11*, resulting in the successful landing of two men on the moon, followed by the crew's safe return. The US would make several more trips to the moon, but the USSR would never match this goal. While it was not the end of the Space Race, the USSR continued to fall behind the US in terms of achievements. Their space program officially ended in 1991.

Other countries had participated in the Space Race, largely working with NASA. Over time, the US and USSR also worked together. This led to much faster progress with things such as the Hubble Telescope and the International Space Station. Unfortunately, without that push, the drive to advance space travel and exploration largely died down during the 1990s. There were some staggering advancements, such as the exploration of Mars by the Mars Exploration Rover, but the pace at which those achievements were reached was much slower than expected. Considering that the US and USSR had first launched a satellite into space in 1957, then managed to land people on the moon by the end of the next decade, there were high expectations that people would be traveling to Mars by the end of the century. Without a serious driver, though, many nations began to decide to put their money toward other efforts. Only during the early

21st century would there be another push to see how far space exploration could be advanced. Nations that had little to do with the first Space Race have begun to more aggressively pursue a presence in space, most notably China, India, and Japan. Some have called this the New Space Race. There has also been a push by private companies to explore space. Since the slow of the original Space Race, these companies seem interested in ensuring that the pace of space exploration continues at a more rapid rate than it has since the 1970s.

Here's another book by Captivating History that you might be interested in

THE HISTORY OF THE UNITED STATES

A CAPTIVATING GUIDE TO AMERICAN HISTORY, INCLUDING EVENTS SUCH AS THE AMERICAN REVOLUTION, FRENCH AND INDIAN WAR, BOSTON TEA PARTY, PEARL HARBOR AND THE GULF WAR

CAPTIVATING HISTORY

Bibliography

1957–58: The Year of the Satellite, NOAA, 2020, Satellite and Information Service, www.nesdis.noaa.gov/

60 years ago, Soviets launch Sputnik 3, Melanie Whiting, May 15, 2018, NASA, www.nasa.gov/

60 Years Ago: Vanguard Fails to Reach Orbit, Mark Garcia, December 6, 2017, NASA, www.nasa.gov/

A look at people killed during space missions, Seth Borenstien, November 1, 2014, Science X Network, phys.org/

A Visual History of Spacewalks, Jeffery Kluger, June 3, 2015, Time Magazine, time.com/

Alouette I and II, Canadian Space Agency, September 28, 2018, www.asc-csa.gc.ca/

An Early History of Satellites Timeline, Broadband Wherever, 2020, NASA, www.jpl.nasa.gov/

Apollo 11: First Men on the Moon, Nola Taylor Redd, May 9, 2019, Future US Inc, www.space.com/

Car crashes, curses, and carousing—the story of the second Soviet in space, Emily Carney, June 16, 2016, arstechnica, arstechnica.com/

Challenger: The Shuttle Disaster That Changed NASA, Elizabeth Howell, May 1, 2019, Future US Inc, www.space.com/

Cosmic Menagerie: A History of Animals in Space, Karl Tate, April 17, 2013, Future US Inc, www.space.com/

Deaths associated with US space programs, January 4, 2019, Airsafe.com, www.airsafe.com/

Development History, Anatoly Zak, 2020, www.russianspaceweb.com/

Did Politics Fuel the Space Race?, Robert Longely, March 20, 2020, Thought Co., www.thoughtco.com/

Explorer 1 Overview, Sarah Loff, Brian Dunbar, August 3, 2017, NASA, www.nasa.gov/

Explorer 1: The First U.S. Satellite, Elizaabeth Howell, August 11, 2017, www.space.com/

'Flight, We Are Docked!' Gemini 8 Achieved 1st Space Docking 50 Years Ago, Robert Z. Pearlman, March 16, 2016, Future US Inc, www.space.com/

From Monkey To Man, Gale, 2020, Cenagage Company, www.gale.com/

Gherman Stepanovich Titov, The Editors of Encyclopaedia Britannica, 2020, Britannica, www.britannica.com/

How NASA Works, Craig Freudenrich, Patrick J. Kiger, 2020, howstuffworks, science.howstuffworks.com/

International Geophysical Year, The Editors of Encyclopedia Britannica, 2020, Encyclopedia Britannica, www.britannica.com/

JFK's 'Moon Speech' Still Resonates 50 Years Later, Mike Wall, September 12, 2012, Future US Inc, www.space.com/

Laika the Dog & the First Animals in Space, Elizabeth Dohrer, May 31, 2017, Future US Inc, www.space.com/

Luna 01, NASA, February 13, 2018, solarsystem.nasa.gov/

Luna 1, Dr. David R. Williams, May 14, 2020, NASA, nssdc.gsfc.nasa.gov/

Lunar Lost & Found: The Search for Old Spacecraft, Leonard David, March 27, 2006, Future US Inc, www.space.com/

March 16, 1966: Gemini's First Docking of Two Spacecraft in Earth Orbit, Sarah Loff, August 6, 2017, NASA, www.nasa.gov/

Missions, Mars Exploration Program, 2020, NASA, mars.nasa.gov/

Moon landing anniversary: How did the historic space race play out?, Lauren Chadwick, July 20, 2019, EuronNews, www.euronews.com/

NASA's Origins & the Dawn of the Space Age, NASA, 2020, history.nasa.gov/

Only Three People Have Died in Space, Amy Shira Teitel, August 20, 2017, Discover, www.discovermagazine.com/

Origins of the Cold War in Europe, Robert Wilde, September 8, 2017, ThoughtCo, www.thoughtco.com/

Profile of John Glenn, Brain Dunbar, August 3, 2017, NASA, www.nasa.gov/

Remembering Belka and Strelka, Tony Reichhardt, August 19, 2010, Air & Space Magazine, www.airspacemag.com/

Roscosmos: Russia's Space Agency, Elizabeth Howell, January 20, 2018, Future US Inc, www.space.com/

Sept. 9, 1955: DoD Picks Vanguard To Launch U.S. Satellite, SpaceNews Editor, June 29, 2004, SpaceNews, spacenews.com/

Sergei Korolev: Father of the Soviet Union's Success in Space, August 3, 2007, European Space Agency, www.esa.int/

Space Race Timeline, Royal Museums Greenwich, 2020, www.rmg.co.uk/

Space Race, Space Next, 2020, Encyclopedia Britannica, www.britannica.com/

Space Race: The Space Rivalry between the United States and Soviet Union and Its Aftermath, Smithsonian, 2020, airandspace.si.edu/

Sputnik 1, Dr. David R. Williams, September 3, 2020, NASA, nssdc.gsfc.nasa.gov/

Sputnik 1, NASA Content Administrator, August 7, 2017, NASA, www.nasa.gov/

Sputnik, 1957, Foreign Service Institute, 2020, Office of the Historian, history.state.gov/

Sputnik: How the World's 1st Artificial Satellite Worked (Infographic), Karl Tate, October 4, 2012, Future US Inc, www.space.com/

Sputnik: The Space Race's Opening Shot, Elizabeth Howell, August 22, 2018, Space.com, www.space.com/

The Apollo Program (1963 - 1972), Dr. David R. Williams, September 16, 2013, NASA, nssdc.gsfc.nasa.gov/

The Gemini Program (1962 - 1966), Dr. David R. Williams, December 30, 2004, NASA, nssdc.gsfc.nasa.gov/

The Launch of Sputnik, 1957, U.S. Department of State, January 20, 2009, 2001-2009.state.gov/

The Luna 1 Hoax Hoax, Tony Reichhardt, January 2, 2013, Air & Space Magazine, www.airspacemag.com/

The Moon and Man at 50: Why JFK's Space Exploration Speech Still Resonates, Mike Wall, May 25, 2011, Future US Inc, www.space.com/

The Sad, Sad Story of Laika, the Space Dog, and Her One-Way Trip into Orbit, Alice George, April 11, 2018, Smithsonian Magazine, www.smithsonianmag.com/

The Soviet Manned Lunar Program, Marcus Lindroos, 2020, FAS, fas.org/

The Soviet Union is first to the Moon, Richard Cavendish, September 9, 2009, History Today, www.historytoday.com/

The Space Race And Man On The Moon, Times Reporter, August 28, 2010, The New Times, www.newtimes.co.rw/

The Space Race of the 1960s, Martin Kelly, March 26, 2020, Thought Co., www.thoughtco.com/

The Space Race, American Experience, 2020, www.pbs.org/

The Space Race, Michael Kernan, August 1997, Smithsonian Magazine, www.smithsonianmag.com/

The Space Race: How Cold War Tensions Put a Rocket under the Quest for the Moon, Science Focus Magazine, 2020, Immediate Media, www.sciencefocus.com/

The Start of the Space Race, Khan Academy, 2020, www.khanacademy.org/

This Is Why Sputnik Crashed Back To Earth After Only 3 Months, Ethan Siegel, November 15, 2018, Starts with a Bang, Forbes, www.forbes.com/sites/

This Is Why The Soviet Union Lost 'The Space Race' To The USA, Ethan Siegel, July 11, 2019, Forbes, www.forbes.com/

This Month in Physics History, American Physical Society, 2020, www.aps.org/

Today in science: 1st spacecraft to moon, Earthsky, January 2, 2017, earthsky.org/

United States-Soviet Space Cooperation during the Cold War, Roald Sagdeev, Susan Eisenhower, 2020, NASA, www.nasa.gov/

Vega 1 & 2, Ron Baalke, 2020, Comets, stardust.jpl.nasa.gov/

Wernher von Braun and the Nazis, Michael J. Neufeld, 2020, American Experience, PBS, www.pbs.org/

Wernher von Braun: History's Most Controversial Figure?, Amy Shira Teitel, May 3, 2013, Aljazeera, hwww.aljazeera.com/

What Was the Space Race?, Adam Mann, August 7, 2019, FutureUS Inc, www.space.com/

Who Was John Glenn?, Brain Dunbar, August 6, 2017, NASA, www.nasa.gov/

Why the U.S. Government Brought Nazi Scientists to America after World War II, Danny Lewis, November 16, 2016, Smithsonian Magazine, www.smithsonianmag.com

Why Yuri Gagarin Remains the First Man in Space, Even Though He Did Not Land Inside His Spacecraft, Cathleen Lewis, April 20, 2010, Smithsonian, airandspace.si.edu/

Will Hitler Be the First Person That Aliens See?, Ross Pomery, September 19, 2013, Real Clear Science, www.realclearscience.com/

Women of NASA, National Geographic, March 2, 2020, National Geographic Society, www.nationalgeographic.org/

Yuri Gagarin: First Man in Space, Jim Wilson, April 13, 2011, NASA, www.nasa.gov/

Yuri Gagarin: First Man in Space, Nola Taylor Redd, October 12, 2018, Future US Inc, www.space.com/

Manufactured by Amazon.ca
Bolton, ON